It's another great book from CGP...

This book contains a brilliant combination of study notes and practice questions
— everything you need to get to grips with KS3 Biology (ages 11-14).

It's ideal if you're working at foundation level — it covers what would
have been called Levels 3-6 in the old Curriculum.

CGP — still the best! ☺

Our sole aim here at CGP is to produce the highest quality books —
carefully written, immaculately presented and dangerously close to being funny.

Then we work our socks off to get them out to you
— at the cheapest possible prices.

Published by CGP

From original material by Paddy Gannon.

Editors:
Rachel Kordan, Rachael Marshall, Sarah Pattison, Rachael Rogers and Sean Stayte

ISBN: 978 1 78294 113 2

www.cgpbooks.co.uk
Clipart from Corel®
Printed by Elanders Ltd, Newcastle upon Tyne.

Based on the classic CGP style created by Richard Parsons.

With thanks to Janet Cruse-Sawyer and Hayley Thompson for the proofreading.

With thanks to Laura Jakubowski for the copyright research.

With thanks to Science Photo Library for use of the image on page 8.

Contents

The Scientific Process

Scientists <u>work scientifically</u> — it's their job. It means they can <u>plan</u> awesome <u>investigations</u>, get <u>useful results</u> and draw <u>scientific conclusions</u> from them. <u>You</u> need to be able to do all that too. Don't worry though. This section will tell you <u>everything you need to know</u>. You'll also be <u>tested</u> on <u>Working Scientifically</u> topics in the rest of the book. Look out for <u>questions</u> with a WS stamp:

A Hypothesis is an Explanation of Something

1) Scientists <u>observe</u> (look at) things they <u>don't understand</u>.

2) They then come up with an <u>explanation</u> for what they've seen.

3) This explanation is called a <u>hypothesis</u>.

Example:

A scientist is looking at <u>why</u> people have <u>spots</u>.

He notices that everyone with spots <u>picks their nose</u>.

The scientist thinks that the spots might be <u>caused</u> by people picking their nose.

Nose picking = spots?

So the <u>hypothesis</u> is: "Spots are caused by picking your nose."

4) Next, scientists need to try to work out whether the <u>hypothesis</u> is <u>RIGHT or NOT</u>.

5) They do this by making a <u>prediction</u> and <u>testing</u> it.

Example:

A prediction is something like: "People who pick their nose will have spots."

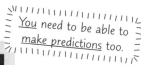
<u>You</u> need to be able to <u>make predictions</u> too.

6) If tests show that the <u>prediction</u> is <u>right</u>, then there's <u>evidence</u> (signs) that the <u>hypothesis is right</u> too.

7) If tests show that the <u>prediction</u> is <u>wrong</u>, then the <u>hypothesis</u> is probably <u>wrong</u> as well.

Other Scientists Test the Hypothesis

1) It's <u>not enough</u> for <u>one scientist</u> to do tests to see if the hypothesis is right or not.

2) <u>Other scientists</u> test the hypothesis as well.

3) Sometimes these scientists will find <u>more evidence</u> that the <u>hypothesis</u> is <u>right</u>.

4) When this happens the hypothesis is <u>accepted</u> and goes into <u>books</u> for people to <u>learn</u>.

New science stuff to learn
I agree...

5) Sometimes the scientists will find <u>evidence</u> that shows the <u>hypothesis is wrong</u>.

6) If this happens, scientists have to either <u>change</u> the hypothesis or come up with a <u>whole new one</u>.

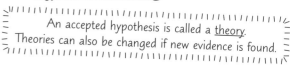
An accepted hypothesis is called a <u>theory</u>. Theories can also be changed if new evidence is found.

Investigations

Scientists do investigations to <u>find things out</u>. You need to be able to do investigations too...

Investigations **Give Us Evidence**

1) Scientists carry out <u>investigations</u> to <u>test</u> their predictions.

2) This gives them <u>evidence</u> to back up their <u>ideas</u>.

3) Investigations can be carried out in a <u>lab</u> or <u>outside</u>.

4) If it's <u>outside</u>, the investigation is usually called <u>field work</u>... though it doesn't always have to be in a field.

Investigations Have to be **Fair Tests**

1) You need to <u>make sure</u> your investigation really <u>tests</u> whether your prediction is <u>right</u> or <u>not</u>.

2) To do this, you must make sure it will be a **FAIR TEST**. This means you must...

> **ONLY CHANGE ONE THING. EVERYTHING ELSE** must be kept the **SAME**.

3) The thing that you **CHANGE** is called the **INDEPENDENT** variable.

4) The things that you <u>keep the SAME</u> are called **CONTROL** variables.

5) The <u>effect</u> that's **MEASURED** is called the **DEPENDENT** variable.

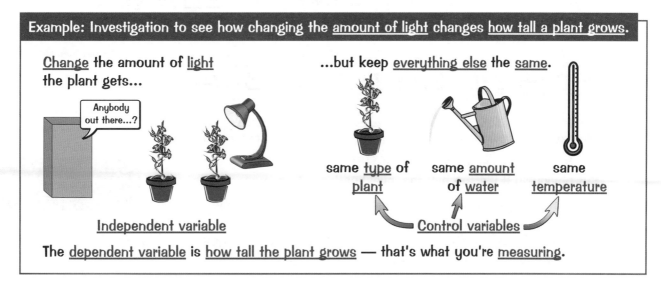

Example: Investigation to see how changing the <u>amount of light</u> changes <u>how tall a plant grows</u>.

<u>Change</u> the amount of <u>light</u> the plant gets...

Anybody out there...?

...but keep <u>everything else</u> the <u>same</u>.

same <u>type</u> of <u>plant</u>   same <u>amount</u> of <u>water</u>   same <u>temperature</u>

Independent variable   Control variables

The <u>dependent variable</u> is <u>how tall the plant grows</u> — that's what you're <u>measuring</u>.

The Equipment Has to be **Right for the Job**

1) You need to choose the <u>right equipment</u> for your investigation.

2) For example, choose <u>measuring equipment</u> that will let you measure stuff <u>accurately</u>.

If you need to measure out <u>11 ml</u>, this measuring cylinder would be great. It's the <u>right size</u> and you can <u>see</u> where 11 ml is.

This measuring cylinder isn't as good. It's <u>too big</u> and you <u>can't really see</u> where 11 ml is.

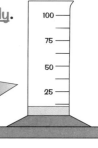

Investigations Can be Hazardous

1) A <u>hazard</u> is something that <u>could cause harm</u>.

2) Hazards include things like <u>bacteria</u>, <u>chemicals</u>, <u>electricity</u> and <u>fire</u>.

3) Scientists need to <u>reduce the risk</u> of hazards causing harm.
   For example, if you're using a <u>Bunsen burner</u>:

- Stand it on a <u>heat-proof mat</u>. This will <u>reduce the risk</u> of starting a <u>fire</u>.
- <u>Turn it off</u> when you're <u>not using it</u>. This will <u>reduce the risk</u> of you <u>injuring yourself</u>.

Investigations Need to be Repeated

1) To <u>back up</u> your <u>hypothesis</u> (see page 2), you need <u>reliable results</u>. Reliable results are:

- <u>REPEATABLE</u> — <u>you</u> get the <u>same</u> or <u>similar results</u> when you <u>repeat</u> your investigation.
- <u>REPRODUCIBLE</u> — <u>other scientists</u> get the same or similar results when they repeat your investigation.
- <u>ACCURATE</u> — really close to the <u>true</u> answer.

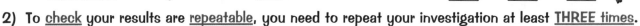

2) To <u>check</u> your results are <u>repeatable</u>, you need to repeat your investigation at least <u>THREE times</u>.

3) Repeatable results are <u>more likely</u> to be <u>reproducible</u>.

4) If you repeat your investigation, you can then work out the <u>MEAN</u> (average) result
   — see next page. This will <u>improve</u> the <u>accuracy</u> of your results.

The Bigger the Sample Size the Better

1) Sample size is <u>how many things are in the group you're testing</u>.
   For example, how many different <u>plants</u> you test, or how many <u>people</u>.

2) The <u>BIGGER</u> the sample size the <u>BETTER</u>.
   But obviously if it's <u>too big</u>, the investigation will <u>take ages</u> to do.

3) It's best if you choose your samples at <u>random</u>. For example:

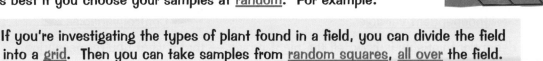

If you're investigating the types of plant found in a field, you can divide the field
into a <u>grid</u>. Then you can take samples from <u>random squares</u>, <u>all over</u> the field.

Errors Can Pop Up if You're Not Careful

1) The results of your experiment will always <u>vary a bit</u> because of <u>random errors</u>
   — tiny differences caused by things like making a mistake when you're measuring.

2) If the <u>same error</u> is made every time, it's called a <u>systematic error</u>. For example...

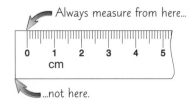

Always measure from here...

...not here.

If you measure from the <u>very end</u> of your <u>ruler</u>
instead of from the <u>0 cm mark</u> every time, <u>all</u>
your measurements would be a bit <u>small</u>.

Organising and Presenting Data

Once you've collected your data (results) you need to <u>organise</u> and <u>present</u> it <u>nice and clearly</u>.

Data *Needs to be Organised*

1) Data needs to be <u>organised</u>
   so that it can be processed later on.

2) <u>Tables</u> are really useful for <u>organising data</u>.

3) You should always make sure that <u>each column</u>
   has a <u>heading</u> and that you've included the <u>units</u>.

Test tube	Volume of gas produced (cm^3)		
	Repeat 1	Repeat 2	Repeat 3
A	28	37	32
B	47	51	60
C	68	72	70

You Might Have to Calculate a Mean

1) When you've done repeats of an experiment you should always calculate the <u>mean</u> (average).

2) You want your results to be as <u>precise</u> (close to the mean) as possible.

3) To calculate the mean <u>add together</u> all the values, then <u>divide</u> by the total number of values.

Test tube	Mass (g)			
	Repeat 1	Repeat 2	Repeat 3	Mean
A	28	37	32	$(28 + 37 + 32) \div 3 = 32.3$

You Can Present Your Data in a Graph or Bar Chart

1) A graph or bar chart makes it easier to <u>spot patterns</u> in your results (see next page).

2) Whatever type of graph or chart you draw, you must choose
   <u>sensible scales</u> for the <u>axes</u> and remember to <u>label</u> them.

3) Make sure you include the <u>units</u> too.

Bar Charts

1) If you're measuring something that comes in <u>categories</u>
   you should use a <u>bar chart</u> to show the data.

2) <u>Categories</u> are things like 'blood group'.
   You <u>can't</u> get results <u>in-between categories</u>.

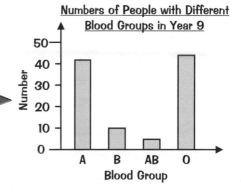

Numbers of People with Different Blood Groups in Year 9

Line Graphs

1) If you're measuring something that can
   have <u>any value</u> in a range you should
   use a <u>line graph</u> to show the data.

2) For example <u>temperature</u> or <u>volume</u>
   could be shown on a line graph.

3) The <u>dependent variable</u> (the thing
   you measure) goes on the <u>y-axis</u>.

4) The <u>independent variable</u> (the thing
   you change) goes on the <u>x-axis</u>.

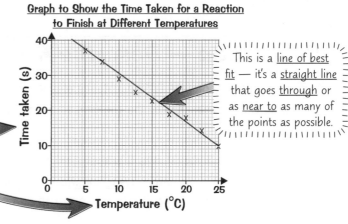

Graph to Show the Time Taken for a Reaction to Finish at Different Temperatures

This is a <u>line of best fit</u> — it's a <u>straight line</u> that goes <u>through</u> or as <u>near to</u> as many of the points as possible.

Working Scientifically

Concluding and Evaluating

Drawing a conclusion is all about <u>finding patterns</u> in your data.

Line Graphs Can Show Patterns in Data

1) When you're carrying out an investigation it's not enough to just present your data — you've also got to find any <u>patterns</u> in the data.

2) Line graphs are great for showing patterns in data.

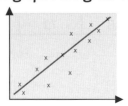 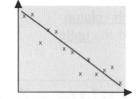 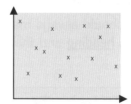

| You can see here that as one variable <u>increases</u> the other <u>increases</u> too. | Here, as one variable <u>increases</u> the other <u>decreases</u>. | There's absolutely <u>no</u> <u>pattern</u> to be seen here... |

A Conclusion is a Summary of What You've Learnt

1) Once you've organised and presented your data, you need to analyse it and come to a <u>conclusion</u>.

2) You just have to <u>look at your data</u> and <u>say what pattern you see</u>.

EXAMPLE: How tall do pea plants grow in three different fertilisers?

Fertiliser	Mean growth / mm
A	13.5
B	19.5
C	5.5

CONCLUSION:
Fertiliser <u>B</u> makes <u>pea plants</u> grow taller than fertiliser A or fertiliser C.

3) You need to use the data that's been <u>collected</u> to <u>justify</u> the conclusion (back it up).

> **EXAMPLE <u>continued</u>:** On average, fertiliser B made the pea plants grow 6 mm taller than fertiliser A and 14 mm taller than fertiliser C.

4) You should also use your <u>own knowledge</u> to try to <u>explain</u> the conclusion.

5) Finally, say whether or not your results <u>back up</u> your original <u>hypothesis</u> (page 2).

Evaluation — Describe How It Could be Improved

In an evaluation you look back over the whole investigation.

1) You should comment on the <u>method</u> — was there anything you could have done better?

2) Write about the <u>quality</u> of the <u>results</u> too — were they all over the place or nice and <u>precise</u>?

3) Then you can suggest any <u>changes</u> that would <u>improve</u> the quality of the results.

4) You might come up with a <u>new question</u> that needs answering too
   — then the whole <u>scientific process</u> starts again.

The Microscope

Learning Objective

Microscopes are fab for looking at teeny tiny things. After these pages you'll be able to...

• use a microscope to look at, identify and record different cell parts.

Microscopes Make Things Look Bigger

1) A microscope is used to look at objects that are too small for you to see normally. For example:

the hairs on a flea

pollen in a flower

cells (see page 10)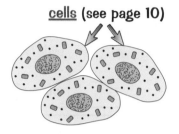

2) A microscope magnifies objects. This means it makes objects look bigger, so you can see them. The more an object is magnified, the more detail you'll see.

3) The microscopes you use in school are light microscopes. They use lenses to magnify objects.

A lens is a specially shaped piece of see-through material — like the glass you get in a pair of glasses.

4) A light microscope has two types of lens:

Eyepiece lens

You look through this to see the object.

Objective lenses

1) There are usually three of these and they're all different lengths.

2) The longer a lens is, the more powerful it is.

3) So longer lenses make things look bigger.

Learn the Different Parts of a Microscope

This is a microscope:

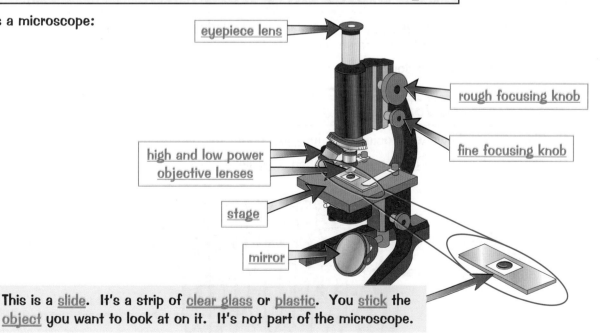

eyepiece lens

rough focusing knob

fine focusing knob

high and low power objective lenses

stage

mirror

This is a slide. It's a strip of clear glass or plastic. You stick the object you want to look at on it. It's not part of the microscope.

Follow These Easy Steps to Using a Microscope

1) Place your microscope near a lamp or a window.
2) Move the mirror so light shines up through the hole in the stage.

> Don't reflect direct sunlight into the microscope — it could damage your eyes.

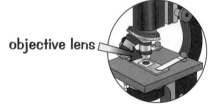

hole in the stage

mirror reflecting light

3) Get your slide — it should have the object you want to look at stuck to it.
4) Clip your slide to the stage.

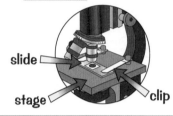

slide

stage

clip

5) Select the lowest-powered objective lens (the shortest one).

objective lens

6) Turn the rough focusing knob to move the objective lens down. Stop when the lens is just above the slide.

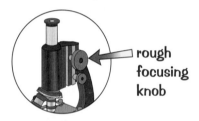

rough focusing knob

7) Look down the eyepiece lens.
8) You will probably need to focus your image (make it look less blurry).

To do this, turn the fine focusing knob until you get the clearest image you can.

eyepiece lens

fine focusing knob

9) If you need to make the image bigger, use a higher-powered objective lens (a longer one).
10) Now refocus the microscope (repeat steps 6 to 8).

Looking at Cells Under the Microscope

1) You need to be able to look at plant and animal cells under the microscope, then identify and record the different cell parts (see pages 10 and 11).
2) This might mean writing down the parts you can see in a table or drawing pictures of them.

Example — Onion Cells Under the Microscope

1) This picture shows what onion cells look like under the microscope.
2) The cells have been dyed purple, so they're easier to see.

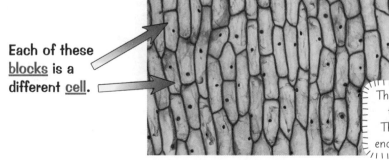

Each of these blocks is a different cell.

There are lots of cell parts you need to learn (see pages 10 and 11). These cells haven't been magnified enough for you to see most of them.

Section 1 — Cells and Respiration

Magic Microscope Questions:

Quick Fire Questions

Q1   What are microscopes used for?

Q2   What is a microscope slide used for?

Practice Questions

Q1   (a)   Label the picture of a microscope below. Use words from the box.

Stage	Eyepiece lens	Focusing knob	Objective lens	Mirror

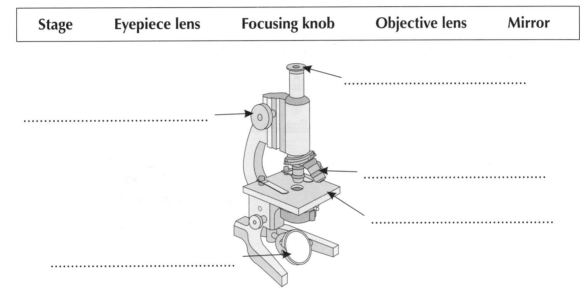

....

....

....

....

....

(b)   Which objective lens makes things look biggest? Circle the correct answer below.

the shortest lens   **the longest lens**

(c)   Apart from the objective lenses, what other part of the microscope
makes things look bigger? Circle the correct answer below.

eyepiece lens   **mirror**   **stage**

Q2   The instructions below say how to focus a microscope on something on a slide.
Write the numbers **1** to **6** in the boxes to put the instructions in the correct order.
Two have been done for you. 1 is the first instruction. 6 is the final instruction.

☐	**Select the lowest-powered objective lens.**
1	**Adjust the mirror so that light shines up through the hole in the stage.**
☐	**Look down the microscope.**
6	**Adjust the focus to get a clear image.**
☐	**Move the objective lens down to just above the slide.**
☐	**Clip the slide onto the stage.**

Topic Review   How did you get on with the questions?
Are you confident on the learning objective?   ☐   ☐   ☐

Section 1 — Cells and Respiration

Cells

This topic is all about <u>cells</u> — and we're not talking about prisons here. By the end of these pages you should...

- understand that <u>all organisms</u> are made of <u>cells</u>
- know the <u>names</u> of different <u>cell parts</u> and understand <u>what they do</u>
- know what's the <u>same</u> and what's <u>different</u> about <u>animal</u> and <u>plant cells</u>
- know <u>what unicellular organisms are</u>, and how <u>adaptations</u> help them to survive.

Living Things are Made of Cells

1) Another word for a <u>living thing</u> is an <u>ORGANISM</u>.
<u>Animals</u> (including humans) and <u>plants</u> are types of organism.

2) <u>All organisms</u> are made up of <u>tiny building blocks</u> called <u>cells</u>.

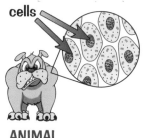

cells

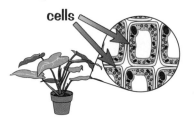

cells

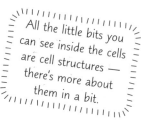

All the little bits you can see inside the cells are cell structures — there's more about them in a bit.

ANIMAL   **PLANT**

3) Cells are <u>so small</u> that you <u>can't see them just by looking</u>. You need to use a <u>microscope</u>.

> <u>Example:</u>
>
> Look at the back of your <u>hand</u>. Your <u>skin</u> is made of <u>cells</u>, but <u>you can't see them</u>. If you looked at a piece of skin <u>under the microscope</u>, you'd be able to see the cells.

Animal and Plant Cells Look Different to Each Other

1) If you're looking at cells under a <u>microscope</u> you'll be able to see the <u>cell structures</u>.

2) You can tell whether you're looking at an <u>animal</u> or a <u>plant</u> cell by the <u>structures</u> it has.

An Animal Cell Looks Like This...

The diagram shows a 'typical' animal cell. They don't all look exactly like this.

An <u>animal cell</u> has:

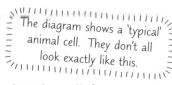

1) A <u>NUCLEUS</u>. This <u>controls</u> what the cell <u>does</u>.

2) <u>CYTOPLASM</u>. This is a sort of <u>jelly</u> that fills the cell. It's where most <u>chemical reactions</u> happen.

3) A <u>CELL MEMBRANE</u>. This is a thin <u>skin</u> around the cell. It <u>holds the cell together</u> and <u>controls</u> what goes <u>in and out</u>.

4) <u>MITOCHONDRIA</u>. These are where <u>aerobic respiration</u> happens. Respiration releases <u>energy</u> for the cell. See page 16.

You need to remember what these cell parts look like — you might be asked to label them on a diagram.

A Plant Cell Looks Like This...

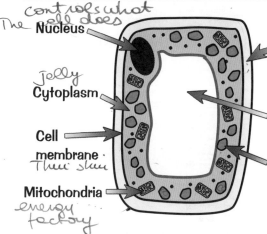

controls what cell does

The Nucleus

Jelly Cytoplasm

Cell membrane *Thin skin*

Mitochondria *energy factory*

Plant cells have a nucleus, cytoplasm, a cell membrane and mitochondria — just like animal cells. But they <u>also have</u>:

1) A <u>CELL WALL</u>. This is a stiff <u>outer layer</u> around the cell membrane. It <u>supports</u> the cell. *thin skin*

2) A <u>VACUOLE</u>. This is filled with <u>cell sap</u>. <u>Cell sap</u> is a liquid containing sugar and salts.

3) <u>CHLOROPLASTS</u>. These are where <u>photosynthesis</u> happens. Photosynthesis makes <u>food</u> for the plant. See page 53.

Animal cells <u>DO NOT</u> have a cell wall, a vacuole or chloroplasts.

Not all plant cells look exactly like this. For example, some plant cells don't have chloroplasts.

Some Living Things Have Only One Cell

'Multi' means <u>many</u> and 'uni' means <u>one</u>.

1) <u>Animals</u> and <u>plants</u> are made up of <u>lots of cells</u>. They're <u>multicellular</u> organisms.

2) But many living things <u>only have one cell</u>. These are called <u>UNICELLULAR</u> organisms.

3) <u>Euglena</u> is a <u>type</u> of unicellular organism. This is a <u>Euglena</u>.

A Euglena lives in <u>water</u>. It has some <u>adaptations</u> (special features) that help it to <u>survive</u>. For example, it has a 'tail' called a <u>flagellum</u>. This helps it to <u>swim</u>.

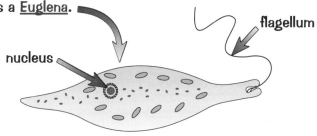

flagellum

nucleus

Super Cell Questions:

Quick Fire Questions

Q1 What is the name of the thin skin around an animal cell?

Q2 Where does aerobic respiration happen in a cell?

Q3 Where would you find cell sap in a plant cell?

Practice Questions

Q1 Look at this diagram of a cell from a pig. Draw arrows on this diagram to join each label to the right bit of the diagram.

nucleus

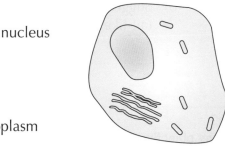

cell membrane

cytoplasm

Section 1 — Cells and Respiration

Q2 Plant and animal cells look different.

(a) Look at this diagram of a cell from a rubber plant.
Use the words below to fill in the missing labels.

cell wall   cytoplasm   vacuole   chloroplast

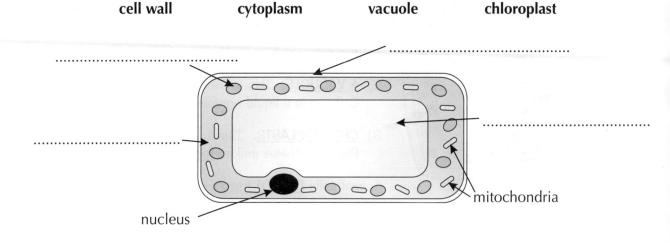

(b) Write down **two** structure that are found in plant cells but **not** in animal cells.

1. ....

2. ....

Q3 Draw lines to match up the first part of each sentence (A, B, C, D) with
the second part of each sentence (1, 2, 3, 4).

A. The nucleus...		1. ...controls what goes in and out of the cell.

B. Chloroplasts...		2. ...are where photosynthesis happens.

C. The cytoplasm...		3. ...controls what the cell does.

D. The cell membrane...		4. ...is where most chemical reactions in the cell happen.

Q4 This is a picture of a type of a bacterium. It lives in water.

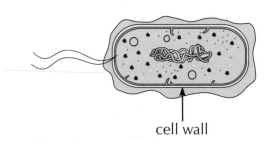

(a) Which word below describes the bacterium?
Circle the answer.

unicellular   multicellular   bicellular

(b) Suggest why the bacterium has the two
tail-like structures.

....

Topic Review How did you find the questions?
Are you happy with all the learning objectives?

Section 1 — Cells and Respiration

Cell Organisation

Learning Objectives

Cells must be great at remembering their homework — they're always so <u>organised</u>. By the end of these pages you should know...

- that cells in <u>multicellular organisms</u> are arranged into <u>tissues</u>, then <u>organs</u>, then <u>organ systems</u>, then the <u>whole organism</u>
- what <u>diffusion</u> is, and how substances <u>move in and out of cells</u> by <u>diffusion</u>.

Cells are Organised

1) <u>Multicellular organisms</u> can contain <u>trillions</u> of cells.

2) The cells aren't all just thrown together in one big blob. They're <u>organised</u> (sorted) into <u>groups</u> so that the organism can work properly. Like this:

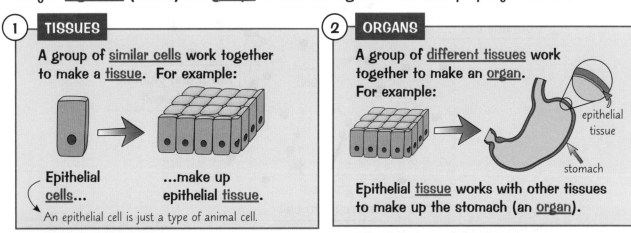

① TISSUES

A group of <u>similar cells</u> work together to make a <u>tissue</u>. For example:

Epithelial <u>cells</u>... ...make up epithelial <u>tissue</u>.

An epithelial cell is just a type of animal cell.

② ORGANS

A group of <u>different tissues</u> work together to make an <u>organ</u>. For example:

epithelial tissue

stomach

Epithelial <u>tissue</u> works with other tissues to make up the stomach (an <u>organ</u>).

③ ORGAN SYSTEMS

A <u>group of organs</u> work together to make an <u>organ system</u>. For example:

The stomach and other organs make up the digestive system (an <u>organ system</u>). See page 25.

④ A MULTICELLULAR ORGANISM

A multicellular <u>organism</u> is usually made up of <u>several organ systems</u>. For example:

The whole human <u>organism</u> has lots of organ systems.

Here's an example from a <u>plant</u>.

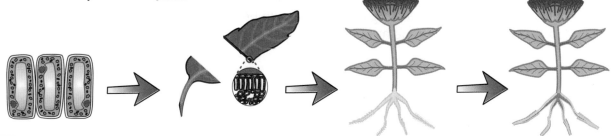

A group of palisade cells (a type of plant cell) make palisade <u>TISSUE</u>.

Palisade tissue works with other tissues to make a leaf (an <u>ORGAN</u>).

Leaves and other organs make up the shoot system (an <u>ORGAN SYSTEM</u>).

Different organ systems make up a plant — an <u>ORGANISM</u>.

Stuff Moves Into and Out of Cells by Diffusion

1) Cells need to <u>take in substances</u> so they can <u>work properly</u>.
They also have to be able to <u>get rid</u> of <u>stuff they don't need</u>.

> **EXAMPLE:**
> Cells need to take in <u>glucose</u> and <u>oxygen</u> for <u>respiration</u> (see page 16).
> They also need to <u>get rid</u> of the <u>carbon dioxide</u> produced.

2) Substances <u>move into</u> or <u>out of cells</u> through <u>little holes</u> in the <u>cell membrane</u>.

3) They can do this by a process called <u>diffusion</u>.

4) Diffusion is where stuff moves from where there's <u>lots of it</u> to where there's <u>less of it</u>.
Just like <u>glucose</u> in this diagram...

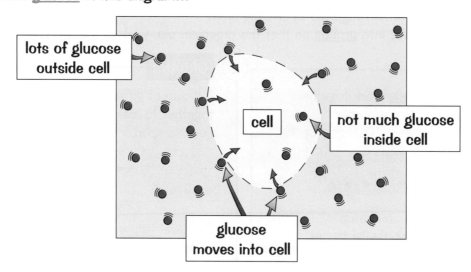

lots of glucose outside cell

cell

not much glucose inside cell

glucose moves into cell

Stunning Cell Organisation Questions:

Quick Fire Questions

Q1 What is an organ system?

Q2 What happens in diffusion?

Q3 True or false? A multicellular organism is usually made up of several organ systems.

Practice Questions

Q1 Below are five different parts of an organism. Write the numbers **1** to **5** in the boxes
to show how the parts are organised. 1 should be the first level of organisation.
5 should be the last. One has been done for you.

☐ organ   ☐ organ system   ☐ tissue   **1** cell   ☐ organism

Q2 A plant root is made of several different tissues that work together.
Is a plant root a **cell**, an **organ** or an **organ system**?

....

Section 1 — Cells and Respiration

Q3 Complete the sentence by choosing the correct word from below the gap.

Cell organisation happens in .... organisms.

unicellular   multicellular

Q4 Which of these sentences about diffusion is **true**? Tick **one** box.

☐ **Diffusion is only needed to move things into a cell.**

☐ **Diffusion is only needed to move things out of a cell.**

☐ **Diffusion is needed to move things into and out of a cell.**

Q5 Give an example of an **organ** in:

(a) a plant ....

(b) an animal ....

Challenge Yourself

Q6 On the right is a group of muscle cells.
They work together to move the muscle.

(a) What would you call a whole group of cells like this?

....

(b) Muscle cells need glucose for energy.
Use the correct words from the box to complete the following passage.

| diffusion | outside | membrane | respiration | inside | nucleus |

There is less glucose .... the muscle cells

than outside the cells. This means that glucose passes through the

cell .... and into the cells. It does this by

a process called ....

Topic Review   How did you get on with the questions?
Have you nailed the learning objectives?

 ☐   ☐   ☐

Section 1 — Cells and Respiration

Respiration

Learning Objectives

Respiration is mega-important — it releases all the energy an organism needs to stay alive. Crikey. By the end of these pages you should know...

- what respiration is and why it's so important
- the word equation for aerobic respiration
- how anaerobic respiration is different from aerobic respiration
- the word equation for anaerobic respiration in humans and in microorganisms
- what fermentation is and when it occurs.

Respiration is a Chemical Reaction

1) In a chemical reaction one or more 'old' substances get changed into new ones. The old substances are called reactants. The new substances are called products.

2) Respiration is a chemical reaction. It happens in every cell.

3) Respiration changes glucose (a sugar) into new substances. This releases energy.

4) The energy released by respiration is used for just about everything. For example:

building proteins   using your muscles   keeping warm

5) There are two types of respiration that you need to know about — aerobic respiration (see below) and anaerobic respiration (see next page).

Aerobic Respiration Needs Plenty of Oxygen

1) Aerobic respiration is respiration using oxygen.

2) It happens in the mitochondria of animal and plant cells (see page 10).

3) In aerobic respiration, glucose and oxygen react to produce carbon dioxide and water. This reaction releases lots of energy.

4) A word equation shows what happens in a chemical reaction. Here's the word equation for aerobic respiration:

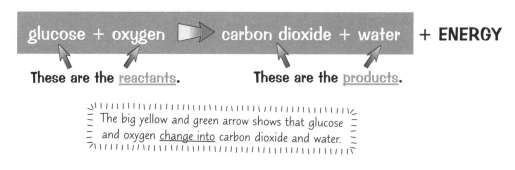

glucose + oxygen ▷ carbon dioxide + water + ENERGY

These are the reactants.   These are the products.

The big yellow and green arrow shows that glucose and oxygen change into carbon dioxide and water.

Section 1 — Cells and Respiration

Anaerobic Respiration **Takes Place** *Without Oxygen*

1) Anaerobic respiration is respiration without oxygen.

2) Anaerobic respiration releases less energy than aerobic respiration.

3) Anaerobic respiration works differently in different organisms:

In HUMANS, anaerobic respiration takes place during hard exercise. It produces a substance called lactic acid.

This is the word equation for anaerobic respiration in humans:

glucose ▶ lactic acid + ENERGY

In MICROORGANISMS like YEAST, anaerobic respiration produces carbon dioxide and ethanol (alcohol).

Here's the word equation:

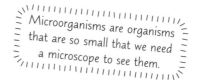

Microorganisms are organisms that are so small that we need a microscope to see them.

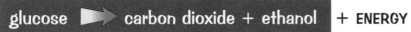

glucose ▶ carbon dioxide + ethanol + ENERGY

When anaerobic respiration produces ethanol, it's called FERMENTATION. Fermentation is the process used to make beer.

Refreshing Respiration Questions:

Quick Fire Questions

Q1 True or false? Respiration takes place in every cell in an organism.

Q2 What is always released by respiration?

Practice Questions

Q1 In what part of animal and plant cells does aerobic respiration take place? Circle the correct answer.

      cell membrane   **nucleus**   **mitochondria**

Q2 Why is respiration so important? Tick the correct answer below.

☐ It releases the energy organisms need to stay alive.

☐ It stops the carbon dioxide level in an organism from getting too high.

☐ It produces glucose for an organism.

Q3 Complete the word equation for **aerobic respiration**. Use the words in the box below.

water	glucose	carbon dioxide

.... + oxygen → .... + ... + ENERGY

Q4 Circle the correct words in bold to complete the sentences below.

Aerobic respiration releases (**more** / **less**) energy than anaerobic respiration.

When you're exercising really hard, (**aerobic** / **anaerobic**) respiration will

start to take place in your muscle cells. This produces (**lactic acid** / **water**).

Challenge Yourself

Q5 A group of students investigated how quickly yeast respired at different temperatures.

They set up the experiment shown on the right.

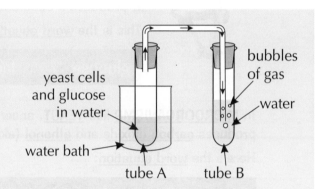

Yeast produce a gas when they respire. The students counted how many bubbles of this gas entered tube B in one minute.

They repeated the experiment three times and worked out the mean of their results.

They changed the temperature of the water bath then did the whole experiment again.

The yeast was respiring **anaerobically** in the experiment.

(a) (i) Write a word equation for this reaction.

.... → .... + ... + ENERGY

(ii) There is another name for this reaction. What is it?

....

(b) Which gas was in the bubbles the students counted? Circle the correct answer.

      hydrogen   **carbon dioxide**   **oxygen**

(c) (i) What was the **independent** variable in the experiment? Circle the correct answer.

    The amount of yeast in tube A.

    The temperature of the water bath.

    The amount of gas that was produced.

(ii) Complete the following sentence:

    Repeating each experiment three times and finding the mean

    makes the results more ....

Topic Review   How did you find the questions? Have you got all the learning objectives sussed?

Section 1 — Cells and Respiration

Nutrition

Learning Objectives

Nutrition is all about getting the food and drink you need to stay healthy. By the end of these pages you should know...

- the seven things you need for a healthy (balanced) diet — these are the five nutrients plus fibre and water

- why each of these things is needed.

A Balanced Diet Contains All These Things

1) Your diet includes everything you eat and drink.

2) You get your nutrition from your diet.

3) You need a balanced diet to stay healthy.

4) A balanced diet will have the right amount of the five nutrients below, as well as fibre and water (see next page).

Cereals are grains such as oats, wheat and rice. We make our breakfast cereals from these.

Nutrient	What it's found in	What it's needed for
Carbohydrates	Bread, potatoes, cereals	Energy — You need lots of carbohydrate if you're active or growing.
Proteins	Meat, eggs, fish	You need proteins to grow and to repair damage.
Lipids (fats and oils)	Butter, cooking oil, cream	Energy — You use lipids for energy if your body runs out of carbohydrates.
Vitamins e.g. Vitamin A, Vitamin C	Vegetables, fruit, cereals	Vitamins keep many important processes happening in your body. For example: • Vitamin A helps you fight against infections, • Vitamin C helps wounds (e.g. cuts) to heal.
Minerals e.g. calcium, iron	For example: • calcium is found in milk, • iron is found in meat.	Minerals are needed for lots of things. For example: • calcium is needed for strong bones and teeth, • iron is needed for healthy blood.

We only need tiny amounts of vitamins and minerals.

	What it's found in	What it's needed for
Fibre	Vegetables, fruit, cereals	Fibre helps food <u>move</u> through your <u>digestive system</u>. If you don't get enough fibre you could get <u>constipation</u> (find it difficult to do poos).
Water	Drinks, watery foods like soup	All the <u>chemical reactions</u> in your body happen in water.

Nutty Nutrition Questions:

Quick Fire Questions

Q1 What do we need carbohydrates for?

Q2 Give **two** examples of foods that contain lipids.

Q3 True or false? Lipids are used for energy.

Practice Questions

Q1 It is important that people include fibre in their diet.

(a) Why is fibre good for the body? Circle the correct answer.

It helps us grow and repair damage.	It gives us strong bones and teeth.	It helps to move food through the digestive system.

(b) Give **one** problem that can be caused by not eating enough fibre.

....

(c) Below is a list of different foods. Underline the **five** foods that are high in fibre.

Cheese   Eggs

Breakfast cereal   Oats

Peas   Beef

Carrots   Butter

Fish   Bananas

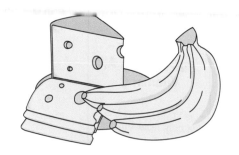

Q2 Why is water needed by the body?

....

Q3 Decide whether each of the sentences below is **true** or **false**.
Tick the correct box.

	True	False
(a) We need to eat a balanced diet to stay healthy.	☐	☐
(b) Iron is a mineral found in meat.	☐	☐
(c) Fruits are a good source of protein.	☐	☐
(d) Eating soup can help the body get enough water.	☐	☐
(e) Vitamins are needed in large amounts.	☐	☐

Q4 Jason has been ill.
His doctor suggests that he needs to get more vitamins.

(a) (i) Give **two** types of food that contain a lot of vitamins.

1. ....

2. ....

(ii) The doctor suggests that Jason should get more vitamin C.
Give **one** benefit of eating vitamin C.

....

Jason's doctor also tells him he needs to get enough minerals in his diet.

(b) Circle the correct word in brackets to complete the sentences below.

(**Calcium** / **Iron**) is needed for strong bones and teeth.

(**Calcium** / **Iron**) is needed for healthy blood.

Q5 Emma has fish and chips for her dinner.

(a) Which is a better source of protein — the fish or the chips?

....

(b) Why do we need to eat protein?

....

Section 2 — Humans as Organisms

More on Nutrition

You need <u>energy</u> simply to stay <u>alive</u>. You also need energy for any extra <u>activities</u> you do, like welly-throwing. After these next few pages you should...

- know how to calculate the amount of <u>energy</u> a person needs each day
- understand that <u>obesity</u>, <u>starvation</u> and <u>deficiency diseases</u> are caused by having an <u>unbalanced diet</u>
- know some of the <u>effects</u> of obesity, starvation and deficiency diseases.

Your Body Needs Energy *All The Time*

1) Your body needs <u>energy</u> to keep it working every day.

2) Even when you're <u>asleep</u> your body has lots of <u>work</u> to do. For example, it has to keep your <u>heart beating</u> and you <u>breathing</u>.

3) You get energy from <u>carbohydrates</u> and <u>fats</u> in your <u>diet</u>.

Different People Have Different *Energy Needs*

1) The <u>heavier</u> you are, the <u>more energy</u> you will need.

2) This is partly because when you're bigger, you have <u>more cells</u> — and every cell needs energy.

3) Also, the <u>more active</u> you are, the <u>more energy</u> you will need.

You Can Work Out Your Daily Basic Energy Requirement

1) Your daily <u>basic energy requirement (BER)</u> is the energy you need every day <u>just to stay alive</u>.

2) It <u>doesn't include</u> the amount of extra energy you need for <u>activities</u>.

3) You calculate BER like this:

Daily BER (kJ/day) = 5.4 × 24 hours × body mass (kg)

kJ means kilojoule — it's a unit of energy.

EXAMPLES

<u>Example 1:</u> A 90 kg man

His daily BER (kJ/day) = 5.4 × 24 hours × body mass (kg)

= 5.4 × 24 × <u>90</u> = <u>11 664 kJ/day</u>

<u>Example 2:</u> A 55 kg woman

Her daily BER (kJ/day) = 5.4 × 24 hours × body mass (kg)

= 5.4 × 24 × <u>55</u> = <u>7128 kJ/day</u>

The woman is smaller than the man — she has <u>fewer cells</u> so she needs <u>less energy</u>.

You Need Extra Energy for Your Activities

1) The more activities you do in a day, the more energy you will need.

2) For example, if you do lots of running and walking, you will need more energy than if you sat on the sofa all day.

3) Different activities need different amounts of energy.

For example, for a 60 kg person:

> Walking for half an hour uses 400 kJ of energy.

> Running for half an hour uses 1500 kJ of energy.

The total amount of energy you need in a day = daily BER + extra energy for activities.

Example:
How much energy does a 60 kg person need in one day if they walk for one hour?

1) Firstly, work out the daily basic energy requirement for someone of that weight.

Daily BER for a 60 kg person = 5.4 × 24 × 60 = 7776 kJ/day

2) Next, work out the extra energy used for activities.

Amount of energy needed to walk for one hour = 400 kJ × 2 = 800 kJ

3) Finally, find the total amount of energy needed.

Total amount of energy = daily BER + energy used in activities
= 7776 + 800 = 8576 kJ/day

> You know that walking for half an hour uses 400 kJ. So to find the energy used in one hour you need to multiply by 2.

An Unbalanced Diet Can Cause Health Problems

Remember, a balanced diet is one that contains the right amounts of nutrients, plus fibre and water. When a diet is unbalanced, it can lead to serious health problems.

Obesity

1) If you take in more energy than you use up, you will put on weight.

2) Over time you could become obese (very overweight).

3) Obesity can lead to health problems such as heart disease.

Starvation

1) Some people don't get enough food to eat — this is starvation.

2) Starvation can cause slow growth in children and irregular periods in women.

Deficiency Diseases

1) Some people don't get enough vitamins or minerals — this can cause deficiency diseases.

2) For example, not getting enough vitamin C can cause scurvy.
This is a deficiency disease that causes problems with the skin and gums.

Mega More on Nutrition Questions:

Quick Fire Questions

Q1 Give **one** effect starvation can have on the body.

Q2 Give **one** example of a deficiency disease and describe its effects.

Practice Questions

Q1 Use some of the words from the box to complete the passage below.

fibre	deficiency diseases	more	food	obesity	minerals

If a person takes in .... energy than they use up, they

will put on weight. Over time, this can lead to ....

If a person doesn't get enough .... to eat, it can lead to

starvation. If a person doesn't get enough vitamins or ....

in their diet, it can cause ....

Q2 Eve has a body mass of 70 kg.

(a) Eve's sister, Amie, weighs 53 kg.
Which sister will have the highest daily basic energy requirement?

....

(b) Calculate Eve's daily basic energy requirement. Use the formula below:

daily BER (kJ/day) = 5.4 × 24 hours × body mass (kg)

Answer: .... kJ/day

(c) Eve swims for half an hour every morning.
For a person with a body mass of 70 kg, swimming uses 1800 kJ per hour.
How much energy does Eve use for swimming each day?

Answer: .... kJ

(d) How much energy does Eve need in total each day?
Use your answers from part (b) and part (c) to help you.

Answer: .... kJ/day

Topic Review Did you feel confident answering the questions?
Have you got all the learning objectives sussed?

Section 2 — Humans as Organisms

Digestion

Digestion is a really <u>important process</u>. It gets all the <u>useful things</u> out of the <u>food</u> we eat. Very handy. By the end of these pages you should know...

- what an <u>enzyme</u> is
- the different <u>tissues</u> and <u>organs</u> that make up the digestive system and how they <u>work together</u> in digestion.

There are Two Steps to Digestion

Digestion is all about <u>breaking food down</u> so we can use the <u>nutrients</u> it contains. It includes:

1. <u>MECHANICAL</u> digestion — this helps to break down food by moving it around or tearing it into pieces, e.g. chewing with teeth:

2. <u>CHEMICAL</u> digestion — this uses <u>enzymes</u> to speed up the chemical reactions that break down food. Enzymes are <u>biological catalysts</u> — this means they <u>speed up chemical reactions</u> in the body.

Your Digestive System is Where Digestion Happens

There are <u>seven organs</u> of the digestive system you need to learn:

1) Mouth

1. <u>Digestion</u> starts here.
2. The food is mixed with <u>saliva</u> (spit).
3. Saliva contains an <u>enzyme</u> that breaks down <u>carbohydrates</u>.

2) Gullet

This <u>links</u> the <u>mouth</u> to the <u>stomach</u>.

3) Stomach

1. Here food mixes with <u>enzymes</u> that break down <u>proteins</u>.
2. The stomach contains muscle (made of <u>muscular tissue</u>). This moves the stomach wall to <u>churn up</u> food — this moves the food around to help break it down.
3. The stomach contains <u>acid</u>. This <u>kills harmful bacteria</u> that are sometimes found in the food we eat.

4) Liver

(see next page)

7) Large intestine

1. After food has been through the <u>small intestine</u>, it comes to the large intestine.
2. Here water is <u>absorbed</u> from the food into the <u>blood</u>.

6) Small intestine

1. Food passes into the small intestine from the <u>stomach</u>.
2. The small intestine makes <u>enzymes</u> to break down proteins, carbohydrates and fats.
3. Food is <u>absorbed</u> from the <u>small intestine</u> into the <u>blood</u>.

Anything that's left over after digestion comes out here as faeces (poo).

5) Pancreas

(see next page)

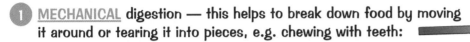
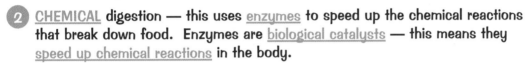

Roles of the Liver and Pancreas

Food doesn't actually pass through the <u>liver</u> or the <u>pancreas</u>, but they're still important organs for digestion.

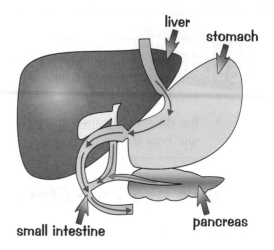

Liver

1) The liver makes a liquid called <u>bile</u>.

2) Bile gets squirted into the <u>small intestine</u>.

3) Bile <u>breaks fats</u> into <u>tiny droplets</u>.

Pancreas

1) The pancreas contains <u>glandular tissue</u>.

2) The glandular tissue makes <u>enzymes</u>.

3) The enzymes are released into the <u>small intestine</u> to help break down food.

⟶ movement of food
⟶ bile
⟶ enzymes from pancreas

Daring Digestion Questions:

Quick Fire Questions

Q1 In which organ does digestion start?

Q2 Name **two** organs in the digestive system that food doesn't pass through.

Q3 Name **two** organs that produce enzymes to digest food.

Practice Questions

Q1 Below are five organs of the digestive system. Number them from **1** to **5** to put them in the order in which food travels through them. One has been done for you.

Organ:	small intestine	stomach	mouth	large intestine	gullet
Order:			1		

Q2 Decide whether each of the sentences below is **true** or **false**.
Tick the correct box.

                                                                    True False

(a) The large intestine links the mouth to the stomach. ☐ ☐

(b) The stomach contains acid to kill harmful bacteria. ☐ ☐

(c) Most food is absorbed into the blood in the small intestine. ☐ ☐

(d) Water is absorbed into the blood in the gullet. ☐ ☐

(e) Food is mixed with saliva in the pancreas. ☐ ☐

Q3 Circle the correct words in the brackets to complete the sentences below.

The pancreas contains (**muscular** / **glandular**) tissue.

This tissue makes (**enzymes** / **saliva**) to break down (**food** / **bacteria**).

Q4 (a) The liver produces a liquid that helps digestion in the small intestine.
What is the name of this liquid?

....

(b) How does this liquid help in digestion?

....

Challenge Yourself

Q5 The mouth and stomach are organs of the digestive system.

(a) Which type(s) of digestion take place in the mouth?

| only mechanical | only chemical | mechanical and chemical |

(b) The stomach contains muscular tissue. How does this tissue help in digestion?
Tick the correct answer.

It produces enzymes to break down fats. ☐

It absorbs digested food into the blood. ☐

It moves the stomach wall to churn up food. ☐

(c) (i) By the time that food leaves the stomach, **two** types of nutrient have already started to be broken down. Which nutrients are these? Circle the correct answers.

| vitamins | proteins | carbohydrates |

(ii) Enzymes are involved in the breakdown of these nutrients.
Why are enzymes important in chemical reactions in the body, such as digestion?

....

....

Topic Review How did you find the questions?
Are you happy with all the learning objectives?

 ☐   ☐   ☐

Section 2 — Humans as Organisms

More on Digestion

Learning Objectives

All the organs involved in digestion are important, but the <u>small intestine</u> is <u>really important</u>. It's where food gets <u>absorbed</u> into the <u>blood</u>. You should learn...

- why the <u>small intestine</u> is good at <u>absorbing</u> food
- the benefits of having <u>bacteria</u> in the digestive system.

*Food Molecules **Get Absorbed** in the Small Intestine*

1) The nutrients in our diet are all different types of <u>molecule</u>.

2) Some of these molecules are <u>big</u>, for example, <u>fats</u>, <u>proteins</u> and some <u>carbohydrates</u>.

3) <u>Big</u> food molecules <u>can't</u> fit through the <u>small intestine wall</u>.

4) So enzymes <u>break up</u> the <u>big molecules</u> into <u>smaller molecules</u>. For example, enzymes break proteins into smaller bits.

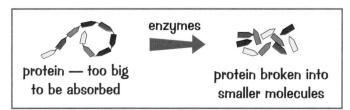

protein — too big to be absorbed → enzymes → protein broken into smaller molecules

5) The small molecules <u>pass through</u> the small intestine wall into the <u>blood</u>.

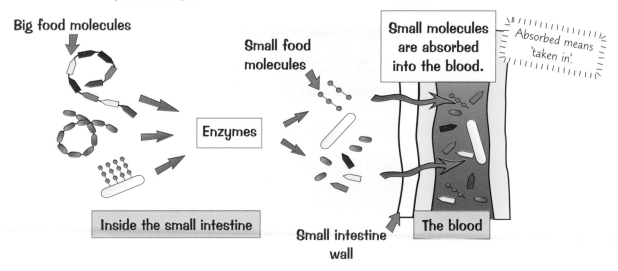

Big food molecules

Small food molecules

Small molecules are absorbed into the blood.

Absorbed means 'taken in'.

Enzymes

Inside the small intestine

Small intestine wall

The blood

*Small Food Molecules **Are Used** by the Body*

1) Once they've been <u>absorbed</u> in the <u>small intestine</u>, the small molecules travel round the body in the <u>blood</u>.

2) They pass from the blood into the <u>body cells</u>.

3) The body can then <u>use them</u> for whatever they're needed for. For example, carbohydrates are used for energy (see page 19).

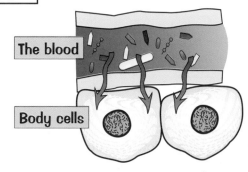

The blood

Body cells

The Small Intestine is Covered with Millions of Villi

1) The wall of the small intestine is lined with tiny finger-like projections (bits that stick out).

2) These are called VILLI.

3) Villi are perfect for absorbing food because:

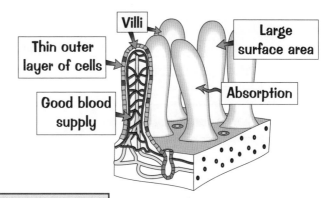

- They have a thin outer layer of cells.
  — so the molecules don't need to travel far to get into the blood.
- They have a good blood supply
  — so the molecules can get into the blood easily.
- They have a large surface area
  — so lots of molecules can be absorbed at the same time.

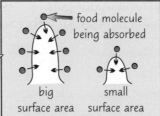

Bacteria are Really Important in the Gut

'Gut' is just another word for 'the intestines'.

1) Bacteria are unicellular organisms (see page 11).

2) It's normal to have loads of bacteria in your gut. These bacteria do a lot of good:

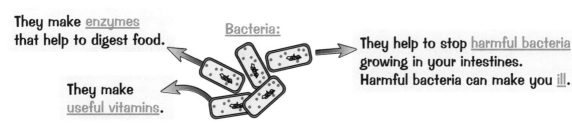

They make enzymes that help to digest food.

Bacteria:

They help to stop harmful bacteria growing in your intestines. Harmful bacteria can make you ill.

They make useful vitamins.

Mighty More on Digestion Questions:

Quick Fire Questions

Q1 How are food molecules transported from the small intestine to the body cells?

Q2 What name is given to the finger-like structures that line the small intestine?

Practice Questions

Q1 Which of the sentences below is **true**? Tick the correct box.

Fats break down big molecules into small molecules. ☐

Big molecules can pass through the walls of the small intestine. ☐

Small molecules are absorbed into the blood. ☐

Q2 Villi have features that make them perfect for absorbing food.
Draw lines to match up the feature with the reason why it's useful.

Feature		Reason it's useful

Thin outer layer of cells

The molecules don't need to travel far to get into the blood.

Large surface area

Lots of food molecules can be absorbed at the same time.

Q3 There are lots of useful bacteria in our guts.
Write down **two** ways in which these bacteria can help us.

1. ....

2. ....

Challenge Yourself

Q4 A starch molecule is made up of lots of small glucose molecules joined together, as shown below.

In the digestive system, starch is broken down into glucose molecules:

(a) What speeds up the chemical reactions that break down starch into glucose?

....

(b) Type 1 diabetes is a condition in which the level of glucose in a person's blood can become very low. If this happens, the person is advised to eat something to raise their blood glucose level quickly. In this situation, do you think it would be better for a person to immediately eat a food high in starch or high in glucose? Explain your answer.

....

....

....

....

....

Topic Review How did you get on with the questions?
Have you nailed the learning objectives?

The Skeleton and Muscles

Learning Objectives

The human skeleton is made of lots of <u>bones</u>. Muscles <u>attach</u> on to these bones and help us to <u>move</u> around. By the end of these few pages you should know...

- what the <u>human skeleton</u> looks like
- the <u>four</u> important <u>jobs</u> of the skeleton
- how muscles use <u>force</u> to <u>move</u> the skeleton
- an example of <u>antagonistic muscles</u> and how they <u>work against each other to move a bone</u>.

The Skeleton Has Four Main Jobs

All the <u>bones</u> in your body make up your <u>skeleton</u>.
The skeleton's jobs are:

1 PROTECTION:

Bone is <u>tough</u>, so it can <u>protect organs</u>. For example, the <u>skull</u> protects the <u>brain</u>.

2 SUPPORT:

Bones are <u>rigid</u> (they can't bend). This means they can support the rest of the body — which lets us <u>stand up</u>.

The skeleton is a bit like a coat hanger — it is a <u>frame</u> for the rest of the body to <u>hang off</u>.

3 MAKING BLOOD CELLS:

Many bones contain a soft tissue called <u>bone marrow</u>. Bone marrow makes <u>red blood cells</u> and <u>white blood cells</u>.

<u>Bone marrow</u> is found in the centre of the bone.

4 MOVEMENT:

<u>Muscles</u> are <u>attached</u> to bones. The action of muscles lets the skeleton <u>move</u>.

Labels: Jaw, Skull, Collarbone, Backbone, Breast bone, Rib, Humerus, Femur, Kneecap, Muscles

Muscles Move Bones

1) <u>Muscles</u> are attached to bones with <u>tough bands</u> called <u>tendons</u>.
2) When a <u>muscle contracts</u> (tightens) it <u>pulls</u> the bone it's attached to.
3) This applies a <u>force</u> to the bone, which can be <u>measured</u>.
4) It also makes the <u>bone move</u>.

The arm: Muscle, Tendon, Bone

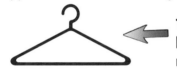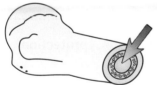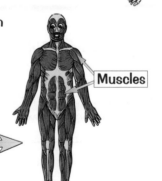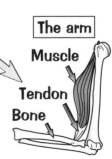

Antagonistic Muscles Work in Pairs

1) Antagonistic muscles are pairs of muscles that work against each other.

2) When one muscle in the pair contracts, the other one relaxes.

EXAMPLE:

The biceps and triceps muscles in the arm work together to bend and straighten the arm.

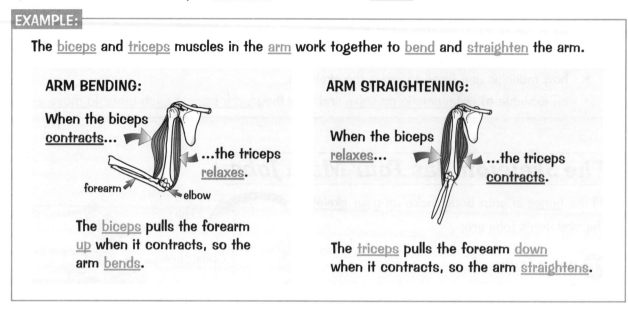

ARM BENDING:

When the biceps contracts...

...the triceps relaxes.

forearm   elbow

The biceps pulls the forearm up when it contracts, so the arm bends.

ARM STRAIGHTENING:

When the biceps relaxes...

...the triceps contracts.

The triceps pulls the forearm down when it contracts, so the arm straightens.

Splendid Skeleton and Muscles Questions:

Quick Fire Questions

Q1 What part of the skeleton protects the brain?

Q2 Bones can produce blood cells — true or false?

Q3 What is a tendon?

Practice Questions

Q1 What is the main function (job) of muscles? Circle the correct answer.

support   production of blood cells   movement   protection

Q2 Match the names of the bones with the area of the body that they come from. Choose words from the box below.

leg	head	arm	chest

Bone	Area of the Body
Humerus	....
Breast bone	....
Jaw	....
Femur	....

Q3 Below is a diagram of a leg.

quadriceps
(muscle)

tibia
(bone)

Circle the correct word in each bracket to complete the passage below.

The quadriceps is attached to the tibia with a (**muscle** / **tendon**).

When the quadriceps (**contracts** / **relaxes**) it applies a force to the tibia.

This makes the tibia (**contract** / **move**).

Q4 (a) What are antagonistic muscles? Complete the sentence below.

They are pairs of muscles that work ....

(b) The biceps and triceps are an example of a pair of antagonistic muscles.
They move the arm. Write **triceps** or **biceps** in each box to complete the table below.

	To make the arm bend:	To make the arm straighten:
Which muscle contracts?	....	....
Which muscle relaxes?	....	....

Q5 (a) One of the main functions of the skeleton is protection.

(i) Circle the correct word in each bracket to complete the passage below.

The ribs are (**tough** / **soft**). This means they can protect delicate

(**muscles** / **organs**) — for example the (**intestines** / **lungs**).

(ii) The centre of each rib contains bone marrow.
Why do we need bone marrow?

....

(b) Another function of the skeleton is support. Explain how the skeleton supports the body.

....

....

Topic Review Did you sail through the questions without any trouble?
Do you understand all of the learning objectives?   ☐   ☐   ☐

Gas Exchange

Learning Objectives Gas exchange is going on all the time in your body. It's very important for keeping you alive. By the end of this topic you should...

- know all the parts of the gas exchange system and what each part does
- know why the lungs are good at exchanging gases.

The Gas Exchange System 'Swaps' Gases

1) We need oxygen for respiration (see page 16).

2) We also need to get rid of carbon dioxide (a waste product of respiration).

3) Gas exchange is all about 'swapping' these gases. Oxygen moves from the air into the blood. Carbon dioxide moves from the blood into the air.

4) The group of structures used for gas exchange is called the gas exchange system.

Learn These Structures in the Gas Exchange System

Lungs

1) You have two lungs.

2) They're like big pink sponges.

3) Gas exchange happens in the lungs.

Trachea

1) A tube that goes from your throat into your chest.

2) The air you breathe in goes through here.

3) It splits into two tubes called bronchi. (Each one is called a bronchus.)

Intercostal Muscles

1) Muscles between the ribs that move the ribcage.

2) Help you to get air in and out of your lungs.

Bronchus

1) You have one bronchus going to each lung.

2) The bronchi split into smaller tubes called bronchioles.

Bronchioles

Small tubes that carry air to and from the alveoli.

Ribcage

1) Made of bone.

2) Goes right round the front and back of your lungs to protect them.

Alveoli

1) Small air sacs in the lungs.

2) Surrounded by tiny blood vessels.

3) Gas exchange happens here.

Diaphragm

1) A muscle that moves up when it relaxes and down when it contracts (tightens).

2) It helps to get air in and out of your lungs.

Gas Exchange *Happens in the Lungs*

1) <u>Breathing</u> is important for gas exchange.

2) When you <u>breathe in</u>, air goes <u>into</u> the <u>alveoli</u> in your lungs.

3) <u>Oxygen</u> moves from the air you've breathed in, <u>into</u> your <u>blood</u>.

4) <u>Carbon dioxide</u> moves <u>out of</u> your <u>blood</u> and into the <u>air</u> inside your alveoli.

5) The carbon dioxide then <u>leaves</u> your body when you <u>breathe out</u>.

6) The lungs are well <u>adapted</u> for gas exchange: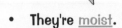

- They're <u>moist</u>.
- They have a <u>good blood supply</u>.
- The <u>alveoli</u> (air sacs) give the lungs a <u>big inside surface area</u>.

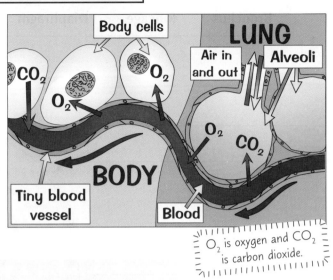

O_2 is oxygen and CO_2 is carbon dioxide.

Graceful Gas Exchange Questions:

Quick Fire Questions

Q1 Name the **two** important gases involved in gas exchange.

Q2 Which structure in the gas exchange system protects the lungs?

Q3 Where in the lungs does gas exchange take place?

Practice Questions

Q1 Four structures found in the gas exchange system are listed below.
Write the numbers **1** to **4** in the boxes to show the order in which air reaches them when you breathe in (1 = first, 4 = last). One has been done for you.

| 1 | Trachea | | Bronchioles | | Alveoli | | Bronchus |

Q2 What is the function (job) of the **diaphragm** in the gas exchange system?
Circle the correct answer below.

It helps to protect the lungs.

It's where gas exchange happens.

It helps to get air in and out of the lungs.

Q3 Fill in the labels on this diagram. Use the words in the box below.

| Bronchus | Ribcage | Diaphragm | Trachea | Alveoli | Intercostal muscle |

Q4 Look at the diagram on the right.

(a) Which arrow, **A** or **B**, represents:

(i) the movement of **oxygen**?

....

(ii) the movement of **carbon dioxide**?

....

(b) Why is it important that these gases are exchanged?

....

....

Q5 List **three** ways in which the lungs are well-adapted for gas exchange.

1. ....

2. ....

3. ....

Topic Review How did you find the questions? Are you happy with the learning objectives?

Section 2 — Humans as Organisms

Breathing

Breathing is how air gets in and out of your lungs. It's easy to do, but there's quite a lot to explain. By the end of these pages you should...

- understand that changes in volume and pressure make air move in and out of the lungs
- understand how movement of the diaphragm and the ribs helps you to breathe in and out
- know what lung volume is and how it can be measured.

A Bit About Volume and Pressure

Breathing happens because of changes to volume and pressure inside the chest. So you need to understand how volume and pressure are linked...

> Volume is the amount of space available inside a container.

1) When air is enclosed in a container it creates pressure.

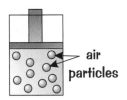

air particles

2) If you increase the volume of the container, the pressure decreases.

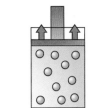

INCREASE IN VOLUME =
DECREASE IN PRESSURE

3) If you decrease the volume of the container, the pressure increases.

DECREASE IN VOLUME =
INCREASE IN PRESSURE

4) Air particles always move from an area of high pressure to an area of low pressure.

The Process of Breathing

The Bell Jar demonstration shows us what's going on when you breathe:

Breathing In

1) Pull the rubber sheet down. This is like contracting your diaphragm.

2) This increases the volume inside the bell jar, which decreases the pressure.

3) The pressure outside the jar is now higher than inside the jar.

4) So air rushes into the balloons, just like air going into your lungs when you breathe in.

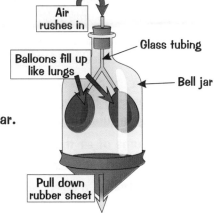

Air rushes in

Balloons fill up like lungs

Glass tubing

Bell jar

Pull down rubber sheet

Breathing Out

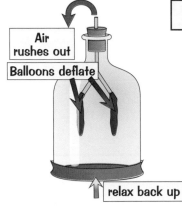

Air rushes out

Balloons deflate

relax back up

1) Let go of the rubber sheet. This is like relaxing your diaphragm.

2) The volume in the jar gets smaller. This increases the pressure.

3) So the pressure inside the jar becomes higher than outside the jar.

4) This means air rushes out of the balloons, like air leaving your lungs when you breathe out.

Inhaling **and** *Exhaling* **is** *Breathing In* **and** *Out*

1) The space inside your <u>chest</u> is like a bell jar.

2) This is what happens when you breathe in and out:

BREATHING IN:	BREATHING OUT:
1) When you <u>breathe in</u>, the <u>diaphragm</u> moves <u>down</u> and the <u>ribs</u> move <u>up</u>.	1) When you <u>breathe out</u>, the diaphragm <u>moves up</u> and the <u>ribs</u> move <u>down</u>.
2) The <u>volume</u> inside the chest <u>increases</u> and the <u>pressure drops</u>.	2) The <u>volume</u> inside the chest <u>decreases</u> and the <u>pressure increases</u>.
3) Air <u>rushes in</u> through the nose or mouth, down the <u>trachea</u> and into the <u>lungs</u>.	3) Air <u>rushes out</u> of your <u>lungs</u>, up the <u>trachea</u> and out of your <u>nose</u> or <u>mouth</u>.

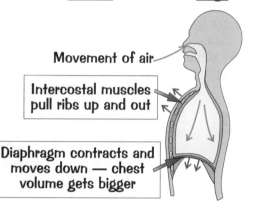

Movement of air

Intercostal muscles pull ribs up and out

Diaphragm contracts and moves down — chest volume gets bigger

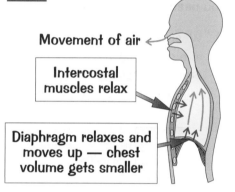

Movement of air

Intercostal muscles relax

Diaphragm relaxes and moves up — chest volume gets smaller

Lung Volume **Can Be** *Measured*

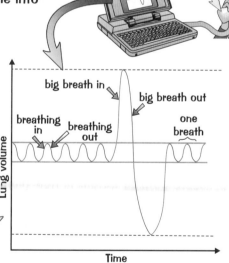

spirometer

1) <u>Lung volume</u> is the <u>amount of air</u> you can breathe into your lungs in a single breath.

2) Lung volume is <u>different for different people</u>. For example, <u>taller</u> people tend to have a <u>bigger</u> lung volume than <u>shorter</u> people.

3) Lung volume can be <u>measured</u> using a machine called a <u>SPIROMETER</u>.

4) To use a spirometer, a person <u>breathes into the machine</u> (through a tube) for a few minutes.

5) The volume of air that is breathed in and out is <u>measured</u>.

6) A graph (called a <u>spirogram</u>) is drawn.

big breath in

big breath out

breathing in

breathing out

one breath

Lung volume

Time

Brilliant Breathing Questions:

Quick Fire Questions

Q1 When is the volume inside your chest bigger — when you **breathe in** or when you **breathe out**?

Q2 What would you use a spirometer for?

Practice Questions

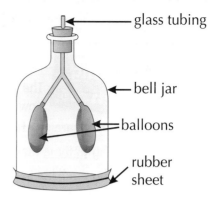

glass tubing

bell jar

balloons

rubber sheet

Q1 Jenny has set up the apparatus on the right to show how the lungs work.

(a) Which part of the apparatus acts like:

(i) the lungs? ....

(ii) the diaphragm? ....

(b) The glass tubing at the top of the jar acts like a structure in the gas exchange system. Suggest which one.

....

(c) (i) Jenny pulls down the rubber sheet. What happens to the balloons?

....

(ii) Complete the sentences to explain why this happens. Use words from the box below.

in	leaves	increases	inflates	out	decreases

Pulling down the rubber sheet .... the volume

inside the bell jar. This .... the pressure inside the

bell jar. Air moves .... through the glass tubing.

The air .... the balloons.

Challenge Yourself

Q2 Answer these questions about the process of breathing.

(a) What happens to the pressure inside your chest when you breathe in?

....

(b) What happens to the lungs when the diaphragm moves down?

....

(c) What happens to the pressure in the chest when the ribs move down?

....

Topic Review Did you feel confident answering the questions? Have you got all the learning objectives sussed?

Exercise, Asthma and Smoking

The gas exchange system is quite a fussy thing — lots of things can affect how well it works. By the end of these pages, you should understand...

- how exercise affects the gas exchange system
- why asthma makes it difficult to breathe
- why smoking is bad for the gas exchange system.

Exercise

1) Exercise affects your gas exchange system.

2) When you exercise, you breathe faster and more deeply.

3) This is so you can get more oxygen to your muscles.

4) More oxygen means that muscle cells can respire more quickly. This releases more energy to keep you going.

Remember, respiration is a process that uses oxygen (and glucose) and releases energy (see page 16).

5) If you exercise regularly these two things happen to your gas exchange system:

1 The muscles you use to breathe get stronger. This helps you to get more air into your lungs.

For example, stronger intercostal muscles will pull your ribs out further when you breathe in. This means more air can fit into your lungs.

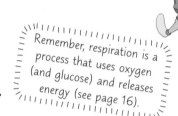

2 You develop more small blood vessels in your lungs — so there's more blood nearby to 'pick up' oxygen. This helps you to get oxygen into your blood faster.

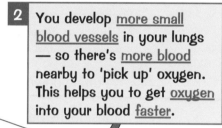

air sacs (alveoli)

small blood vessels

Asthma

1) Asthma is a lung disease.

2) People with asthma have lungs that are too sensitive to certain things (e.g. pet hair, dust, smoke...).

3) If a person with asthma breathes these things in, it affects the bronchioles (tubes in the lungs).

4) This can cause an asthma attack. This is what happens:

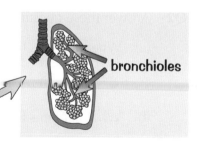

bronchioles

A bronchiole BEFORE asthma attack

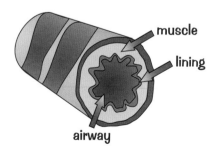

muscle

lining

airway

A bronchiole DURING asthma attack

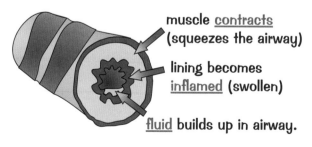

muscle contracts (squeezes the airway)

lining becomes inflamed (swollen)

fluid builds up in airway.

5) These changes narrow the airways. This makes it hard to breathe.

Smoking

When a person smokes a cigarette, the smoke moves through the airways to the lungs.
Cigarette smoke contains tar. Tar is really bad for you:

1) Tar covers the cilia (little hairs) in your airways.
2) Cilia normally wiggle about to move mucus (thick sticky stuff) out of your airways. The damaged cilia can't do this properly.
3) The mucus sticks in your airways.
4) This makes you cough more — it's called smoker's cough.
5) The damage can eventually lead to lung diseases, which make it difficult to breathe.
6) Tar also contains chemicals that cause cancer.

←Cilia

←Mucus

Exotic Exercise, Asthma and Smoking Questions:

Quick Fire Questions

Q1 Why do you start breathing harder when you exercise?

Q2 Asthma is not a lung disease — true of false?

Practice Questions

Q1 Darren has asthma. He is sensitive to dust.

(a) Name **one** other substance that a person with asthma can be sensitive to.

....

(b) What part of the airways is affected by asthma?
Circle the correct answer.

the bronchus   **the bronchioles**   **the trachea**

(c) Tick **three** sentences below that are **true**.

☐ Dust can cause Darren to have an asthma attack.

☐ Darren's airways get wider during an asthma attack.

☐ An asthma attack will make it difficult for Darren to breathe.

☐ Dust could make the lining of Darren's airways become swollen.

(d) What will happen to the muscles around Darren's airways during an asthma attack?
Underline the correct answer.

They will relax.   **They will contract.**   **They will stay the same.**

Section 2 — Humans as Organisms

Q2 Anita's doctor has advised her to start taking regular exercise, so she joins a running club.

(a) Anita notices that her breathing changes while she is running. Suggest how it changes.

....

(b) Complete the following passage to explain why her breathing changes.
Choose the correct word from below each gap.

Anita's breathing changes so she can get more .... into her body.
oxygen / water

Her muscles need this so they can .... more.
respire / relax

This process releases .... to keep her going.
blood / energy

(c) Anita goes running three times a week for 12 weeks.
Read the sentences below about how Anita's body may have changed in this time.
Underline the one that is most likely to have happened.

The number of alveoli in her lungs may have decreased.

She may have developed more small blood vessels in her lungs.

Her ribs may have grown longer.

(d) Anita's intercostal muscles have become stronger.
Describe how this is helpful to Anita while she is running.

....

....

Q3 Smoking can damage the airways of the gas exchange system.

(a) (i) What are the little hairs in your airways called? ....

(ii) What is the job of these little hairs? Circle the correct answer.

| They move mucus out of your airways. | They move mucus into your airways. | They move water into your airways. |

(b) Explain how smoking causes smoker's cough.

....

....

....

Topic Review How did you get on with the questions? Are you confident on all the learning objectives?

Section 2 — Humans as Organisms

Human Reproduction

Reproduction is a very important process — you wouldn't be here without it. You need to know...

- what reproduction is
- what a gamete is
- the parts of the male and female reproductive systems and what each part is for
- how an egg is fertilised

Human Reproduction *Involves a* Male *and a* Female

1) Reproduction is how plants and animals make their young.

2) When mammals (such as humans) reproduce, both a male and a female need to be involved.

3) The male and the female both have a different reproductive system (see below).

4) An important job of each reproductive system is to make sex cells or 'gametes'.

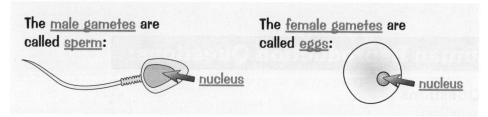

The male gametes are called sperm: nucleus

The female gametes are called eggs: nucleus

5) A sperm and an egg must meet up for reproduction to happen.

The Male Reproductive System

1) Sperm are made in the testes after puberty. (Puberty is the period of life where a child's body develops into an adult's body.)

2) Sperm leave the penis through the urethra during sexual intercourse.

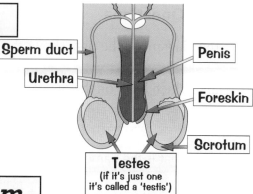

Sperm duct — Penis

Urethra

Foreskin

Scrotum

Testes (if it's just one it's called a 'testis')

The Female Reproductive System

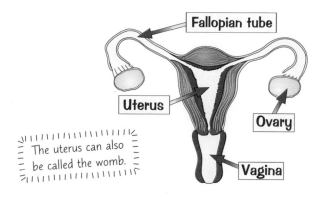

Fallopian tube

Uterus

Ovary

Vagina

The uterus can also be called the womb.

1) Eggs are made in the ovaries.

2) After puberty, an egg is released from an ovary into a fallopian tube every 28 days.

3) This is part of the menstrual cycle (see page 46 for more).

An Egg May be Fertilised After Sexual Intercourse

1) <u>Sperm</u> are released from the penis into the <u>vagina</u> during <u>sexual intercourse</u>.

2) They then travel to a <u>fallopian tube</u>, where they might meet an <u>egg</u>.

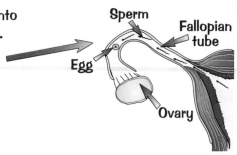

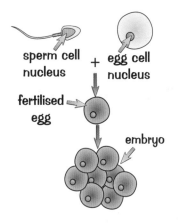

3) The <u>nucleus</u> of a <u>sperm cell</u> and the <u>nucleus</u> of an <u>egg cell</u> may then <u>combine</u>. This is **FERTILISATION**.

4) The fertilised egg <u>divides</u> to become a <u>ball of cells</u>. This ball of cells is called an **EMBRYO**.

5) The embryo develops into a baby in the **UTERUS**.

6) If an egg is <u>not fertilised</u>, it will <u>break down</u> and pass out of the vagina during a <u>period</u> (see page 46).

Handy Human Reproduction Questions:

Quick Fire Questions

Q1 What are male gametes called?

Q2 Where are female gametes made?

Practice Questions

Q1 The diagram on the right shows the male reproductive system.

(a) Which letter on the diagram points to the penis?

....

(h) What is the name of the structure marked **B** on the diagram?

....

(c) (i) Which letter shows a structure that produces sperm? ....

(ii) What is this structure called?

....

(d) Describe the role of structure **D** in reproduction.

....

....

Q2 The diagram below shows the female reproductive system.
Use the words from the box below to label the diagram.

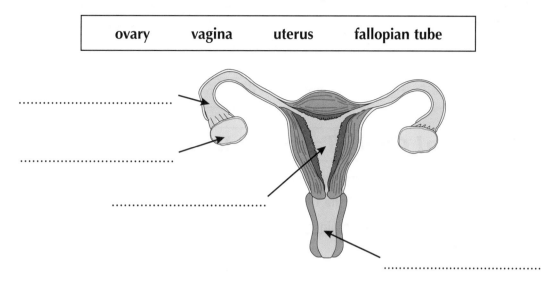

| ovary | vagina | uterus | fallopian tube |

....

....

....

....

Q3 Following sexual intercourse, a woman may become pregnant.

(a) In which part of the female reproductive system does fertilisation of the egg take place?

....

(b) The baby develops in the womb. Give another name for the womb.

....

(c) What happens to an egg if it is not fertilised by a sperm cell?

....

....

Q4 (a) What happens in fertilisation?

....

....

(b) The fertilised egg divides into a ball of cells. What is the name given to this ball of cells?

....

Topic Review | How did you get on with the questions? Have you nailed the learning objectives? | | |

46

The Menstrual Cycle

Learning Objectives

The <u>menstrual cycle</u> happens <u>every month</u> in <u>women</u> who have reached puberty. By the end of these pages you should know...

- what happens in each of the <u>four main stages</u> of the <u>menstrual cycle</u>
- <u>when</u> each of the <u>four stages</u> happens within the menstrual cycle.

The Menstrual Cycle Takes 28 Days

1) In the menstrual cycle, the body <u>prepares</u> the uterus in case it receives a <u>fertilised egg</u>.

2) If this doesn't happen, the <u>lining</u> of the uterus <u>breaks down</u> and the woman has a <u>period</u> (see below).

3) The diagram below shows the <u>four main stages</u> of the menstrual cycle:

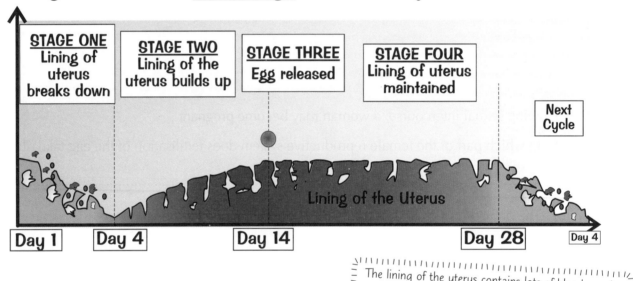

STAGE ONE Lining of uterus breaks down

STAGE TWO Lining of the uterus builds up

STAGE THREE Egg released

STAGE FOUR Lining of uterus maintained

Next Cycle

Lining of the Uterus

Day 1 Day 4 Day 14 Day 28 Day 4

The lining of the uterus contains lots of blood vessels. That's why a woman 'bleeds' during a period.

Stage One — Starts on Day 1

1) <u>BLEEDING STARTS</u>. The <u>lining of the uterus breaks down</u> and passes out of the vagina.

2) This is called "having a <u>PERIOD</u>". It usually lasts <u>3 to 4 days</u>.

Stage Two — Starts on Day 4

1) The <u>lining</u> of the <u>uterus</u> starts to <u>build up</u> again.

2) This makes it nice and <u>thick</u>, ready for a <u>fertilised egg</u> to land there. The egg may then develop into a baby — see page 48.

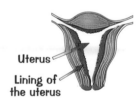

Uterus

Lining of the uterus

Stage Three — Day 14

An <u>egg is released</u> from the ovaries. It may now be fertilised.

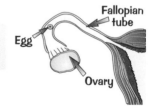

Fallopian tube

Egg

Ovary

Stage Four — Starts on Day 15

1) The lining of the uterus is <u>maintained</u> (kept thick).

2) If a fertilised egg doesn't land there, the lining will <u>break down</u> and pass out of the vagina. Then the whole cycle <u>starts again</u>.

Section 2 — Humans as Organisms

Merry Menstrual Cycle Questions:

Quick Fire Questions

Q1 How long does the menstrual cycle usually take?

Q2 What happens to the uterus lining between day 15 and day 28 of the menstrual cycle?

Practice Questions

Q1 Once a girl enters puberty, she goes through the menstrual cycle every month.

(a) Which statement below gives the correct definition of the menstrual cycle?
Circle the answer.

A period.

The breakdown of the wall of the uterus.

The monthly reproductive cycle in a female.

The process by which a baby is made.

(b) On approximately which **day** of the menstrual cycle does each of these events take place?

(i) An egg is released by an ovary.   ....

(ii) The lining of the uterus starts to thicken.   ....

(iii) The 'period' starts.   ....

Q2 During the menstrual cycle, the lining of the uterus becomes thicker then breaks down.

(a) Why does the lining of the uterus become thicker?

....

....

(b) (i) During which **stage** of the menstrual cycle does the lining of the uterus break down?

....

(ii) What happens to the lining of the uterus once it has broken down?

....

(iii) Roughly how long does this stage last?

....

Topic Review Did you feel confident answering the questions?
Have you got all the learning objectives sussed?

Section 2 — Humans as Organisms

Having a Baby

It takes a while for a baby to <u>develop</u> inside the mother. During this time the mother's lifestyle can <u>affect</u> the baby. You should know...

- how an <u>embryo develops</u> throughout <u>gestation</u> up until its <u>birth</u>
- what the <u>placenta</u> is, and how a pregnant woman's <u>lifestyle</u> can <u>affect her foetus</u>.

Gestation Lasts For 39 Weeks

1) The time between the <u>egg being fertilised</u> and the <u>baby being born</u> is called <u>GESTATION</u> (or pregnancy).

2) Once a fertilised egg has developed into an <u>embryo</u> (see page 44), it <u>implants</u> (sticks itself) into the <u>uterus lining</u>.

3) The embryo then starts to <u>grow</u>...

embryo   uterus lining

At 1 Month

 The embryo is 6 mm long. It has a <u>brain</u>, <u>heart</u>, <u>eyes</u>, <u>ears</u> and <u>legs</u>.

At 9 Weeks

 The body is about 25 mm long. It is <u>completely formed</u> — it's now called a <u>FOETUS</u>.

At 3 Months

 The foetus is 54 mm long. It looks <u>much more</u> like a <u>baby</u>.

At 5 Months

It's now about 160 mm long. It <u>kicks</u> its legs.

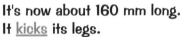

At 7 Months

 The foetus is 370 mm long. It would probably <u>survive</u> if it were born now.

At 39 weeks

The baby is about 520 mm long. It's ready to be <u>BORN</u>.

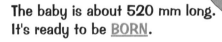

A Pregnant Woman's Lifestyle is Important

1) A <u>placenta</u> is the organ that attaches to the <u>uterus lining</u> when an embryo has formed.

2) The placenta lets the foetus get <u>things it needs</u> from its <u>mother's blood</u>. For example, <u>food</u> and <u>oxygen</u>.

3) But <u>harmful chemicals</u> can also get from the mother's blood to the foetus <u>through the placenta</u>.

4) Harmful chemicals get into the mother's blood if she <u>smokes</u>, <u>drinks alcohol</u> or takes <u>other drugs</u>.

5) These chemicals can <u>harm the foetus</u>. For example, if a pregnant woman <u>smokes</u>:

- there's more chance her baby will be born <u>before it's properly developed</u> — so it might be quite <u>small</u>.

- the baby may have <u>problems breathing</u>.

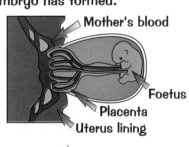

Mother's blood

Foetus

Placenta

Uterus lining

Helpful Having a Baby Questions:

Quick Fire Questions

Q1 Describe what 'gestation' is.

Q2 Where should an embryo implant?

Q3 True or false? Drinking alcohol during pregnancy could harm the foetus.

Practice Questions

Q1 An embryo develops into a baby during pregnancy.

(a) What name is given to the embryo when it is completely formed.
Circle the correct answer.

| placenta | egg | foetus |

(b) Write the correct **number** in each gap to complete the sentences below.

After fertilisation, it takes around .... weeks until the baby

is ready to be born. However, the baby would probably survive if it was

born after .... months.

(c) Women are advised not to smoke during pregnancy. State **two** negative effects that smoking during pregnancy could have on the baby when it is born.

1. ....

2. ....

Q2 Below is a diagram of a foetus attached to the uterus lining of its mother.

(a) Draw an arrow to the **placenta** and label it.

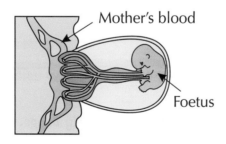

Mother's blood

Foetus

(b) Give **one** reason why the placenta is important to the developing baby.

....

Topic Review — How did you find the questions?
Are you happy with all the learning objectives?

Section 2 — Humans as Organisms

Health and Drugs

Misusing drugs can cause really big problems for people who take them — they can destroy people's health and ruin lives. Make sure you know...

- what a drug is and what is meant by a recreational drug
- how the misuse of drugs can affect life processes, health and behaviour.

Health is More Than Just Not Being Ill

1) Good health means having: ➤
   - A healthy body that's all working properly with no diseases.
   - A healthy mind so you can cope with the ups and downs of life.

2) Taking drugs can affect your health.

Drugs

1) A drug is anything that affects the way the body works. For example, a drug may increase heart rate.

2) Drugs can affect LIFE PROCESSES. For example, drugs that affect the brain are likely to affect movement and sensitivity.

3) RECREATIONAL DRUGS are drugs used for fun. They can be legal (like alcohol) or illegal (like ecstasy).

> **7 Life Processes**
> Movement — moving parts of the body.
> Reproduction — producing offspring.
> Sensitivity — responding and reacting.
> Nutrition — getting food to stay alive.
> Excretion — getting rid of waste.
> Respiration — turning food into energy.
> Growth — getting to adult size.

Solvents

1) Solvents are found in things like paints and glues.

2) Sniffing solvents can make you see and hear things that are not really there. Misusing solvents like this can affect your behaviour.

3) Solvents also damage the lungs, brain and kidneys.

Alcohol

1) Alcohol is found in beers, wines and spirits.

2) It decreases brain activity. This means you react to things more slowly.

3) It can damage the brain and liver.

4) It impairs judgement — so you might end up doing silly things.

Illegal Drugs

1) There are many illegal recreational drugs. For example, ecstasy, heroin and LSD.

2) Many illegal drugs are very addictive. This means the user feels like they NEED to have them.

3) They affect behaviour.

4) They can have very bad effects on a person's body. For example, ecstasy can lead to dehydration (not enough water in the body), which can cause DEATH.

Dangerous (Health and) Drugs Questions:

Quick Fire Questions

Q1 What is a recreational drug?

Q2 Name **two** life processes that can be affected by drugs that affect the brain.

Q3 Name an organ that can be damaged by drinking too much alcohol.

Practice Questions

Q1 Read the statements below. Draw a circle around the **three** that are **true**.

> **Drugs can affect life processes.**
>
> **All recreational drugs are illegal.**
>
> **Drugs can damage your health.**
>
> **Alcohol is a drug.**
>
> **All drugs are things you swallow.**

Q2 Taking drugs can affect your health.

(a) Complete the sentences below about good health.

Good health means having a healthy .... that's working

properly with no diseases. It also means having a healthy ....

so you can cope with the ups and downs of life.

(b) What is a drug? Circle the correct answer.

| A substance that affects the brain. | Anything that affects the way the body works. | A substance that makes you feel better. |

(c) Some drugs are illegal, like ecstasy.

(i) Name **two** other illegal drugs.

1. ....   2. ....

(ii) Give **one** negative effect ecstasy can have on the body.

....

(d) What does it mean if a drug is described as being addictive?

....

....

Q3 Solvents can be found in everyday items.

(a) Give **one** example of a product that contains solvents.

....

(b) How can misusing solvents affect your behaviour?

....

....

(c) Name **two** organs of the body that can be damaged by misusing solvents.

1. ....

2. ....

Q4 A scientist is investigating how alcohol affects the length of time it takes people to react. (WS)
He measured six people's reaction time before and after they had an alcoholic drink.
His results are shown in the table below.

	Reaction time (seconds)					
	Person 1	Person 2	Person 3	Person 4	Person 5	Person 6
Before drinking	0.50	0.35	0.55	0.43	0.37	0.47
After drinking	0.56	0.43	0.67	0.49	0.42	0.56

(a) (i) When did each person react fastest — before or after drinking the alcohol?

....

(ii) Complete the sentences below by circling the correct word in the brackets.

Alcohol (**increases** / **decreases**) brain activity.

This means you react to things more (**slowly** / **quickly**).

(b) The scientist thinks his results show that alcohol affects one of the life processes.
Which life process do you think this is? Explain your answer.

....

....

(c) How could the scientist check his results are repeatable?

....

....

Topic Review How did you get on with the questions? Are you confident on all the learning objectives?

Section 2 — Humans as Organisms

Plant Nutrition

Learning Objectives

Plants are quite amazing really. Pretty much all they need to stay happy is <u>sunshine</u>, <u>water</u>, <u>air</u> and <u>soil</u>. Simple. You should know...

* that plants make (food) (carbohydrate) by <u>photosynthesis</u>
* the <u>word equation</u> for <u>photosynthesis</u> and what the <u>reactants</u> and <u>products</u> are
* some of the things that make leaves <u>good at photosynthesis</u> — including how <u>stomata</u> let <u>gases</u> in and out of a leaf
* that plants get <u>water</u> and <u>minerals</u> from the soil through their <u>roots</u>.

Photosynthesis *Makes Food* From *Sunlight*

1) Just like animals, plants need <u>nutrition</u> to keep them <u>alive</u> and <u>healthy</u>. Instead of eating, plants make their own <u>food</u> using <u>photosynthesis</u>.
2) Photosynthesis is a <u>chemical process</u>. It takes place in <u>every green plant</u>.
3) Photosynthesis produces food in the form of <u>glucose</u> (a <u>carbohydrate</u>). Plants need this glucose so they can <u>grow</u>.
4) Photosynthesis happens <u>mainly in the leaves</u>.

Four Things *are Needed* for *Photosynthesis...*

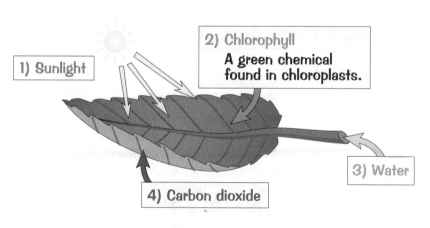

1) Sunlight

2) Chlorophyll
A green chemical found in chloroplasts.

3) Water

4) Carbon dioxide

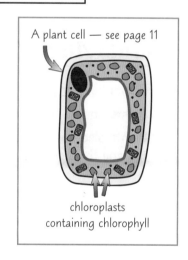

A plant cell — see page 11

chloroplasts
containing chlorophyll

1) <u>Chlorophyll</u> absorbs <u>sunlight</u>.
2) Photosynthesis uses the <u>energy</u> from <u>sunlight</u> to turn <u>carbon dioxide</u> and <u>water</u> into <u>glucose</u>. <u>Oxygen</u> is also made.
3) You can write this <u>word equation</u> to show what happens:

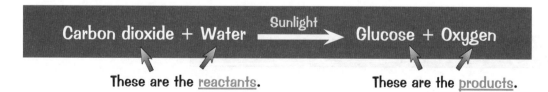

Carbon dioxide + Water —Sunlight→ Glucose + Oxygen

These are the <u>reactants</u>.   These are the <u>products</u>.

4) In a chemical reaction, the <u>reactants</u> are the chemicals you <u>started</u> with. The <u>products</u> are the chemicals you <u>end</u> up with.
5) So in <u>photosynthesis</u>, the <u>reactants</u> are <u>carbon dioxide</u> and <u>water</u>. The <u>products</u> are <u>glucose</u> and <u>oxygen</u>.

Leaves are Great at Photosynthesis

Leaves have some adaptations (special features) which make them really good at photosynthesis.
For example...

1) Leaves are usually broad. This gives them a big surface area for absorbing light.

BROAD LEAF

NARROW LEAF

2) Leaves have lots of chloroplasts. These are mainly near the top of the leaf, where there's most light.

INSIDE A LEAF...

oxygen out

carbon dioxide in

3) The bottom of the leaf has lots of tiny holes called stomata. These let carbon dioxide move into the leaf from the air. They also let oxygen move out.

Plants Also Need Things from the Soil

1) Plants need minerals from the soil to keep healthy.

2) Plants absorb minerals through their roots.

3) Plants also absorb water from the soil through their roots.

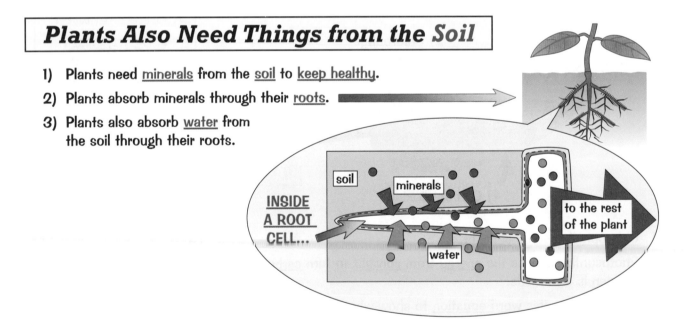

INSIDE A ROOT CELL...

soil

minerals

water

to the rest of the plant

Pesky Plant Nutrition Questions:

Quick Fire Questions

Q1 What is the name of the food that plants make for themselves?

Q2 Which structures in a plant cell contain chlorophyll?

Q3 What are stomata? What do they do?

Practice Questions

Q1 What **two** substances do plants absorb through their roots?
Tick the correct answers.

☐ sunlight   ☐ water   ☐ carbon dioxide   ☐ minerals   ☐ oxygen

Q2 Plants make their own food by photosynthesis.

Complete the following word equation for photosynthesis.
Use words from the box on the right.

oxygen	water
	glucose

.... + carbon dioxide $\xrightarrow{\text{sunlight}}$ .... + ...

Q3 Complete the passage below by circling the correct word in each set of brackets.

Most photosynthesis in a plant happens in the leaves. Leaves are usually (**broad / narrow**),

which means they have a (**large / small**) surface area. This helps them to absorb more

(**light / minerals**). Most (**chloroplasts / stomata**) are found near the top of the leaf.

This is because this is where there is the most (**light / oxygen**).

Challenge Yourself

Q4 James and Jessica are each given a bean plant. James puts his on the windowsill
in his bedroom. Jessica puts hers in a cupboard. Both plants are watered regularly.
After several weeks, James' plant has grown much bigger. Jessica's plant has died.

(a) Suggest why James' plant has grown bigger but Jessica's has died.

....

....

....

....

(b) James wants to investigate whether other plants will grow in the same way as the bean
plants when they are kept on a windowsill compared to in a cupboard. He makes a
prediction for his investigation. Complete his prediction, which has been started below.

Over several weeks, plants that are kept on a windowsill will .... (WS)

....

Topic Review How did you get on with the questions?
Are you confident on all the learning objectives?

☺☐   ☺☐   ☺☐

Plant Reproduction

Plants need to <u>reproduce</u> to make more of themselves, just like animals do. Make sure you...

- know the <u>male</u> and <u>female</u> parts of a <u>flower</u>
- know what <u>pollination</u> is
- understand how plants can be <u>pollinated</u> by <u>insects</u> or by the <u>wind</u>.

The *Flower* Contains the *Reproductive Organs*

1) <u>Sexual reproduction</u> (in plants and animals) happens when a <u>male</u> sex cell and a <u>female</u> sex cell <u>come together</u> (see page 43).

2) Most <u>animals</u> only make <u>one type</u> of sex cell depending on whether they are male or female.

3) <u>Plants</u> are <u>different</u>. Most flowering plants make <u>BOTH male and female</u> sex cells.

4) In these plants both types of sex cell are made in the <u>flowers</u>. The flowers have <u>male parts</u> and <u>female parts</u>...

1) Stamens

1) The <u>male</u> parts of the flower.

2) The stamens are made of the <u>anther</u> and the <u>filament</u>.

3) The anther contains <u>POLLEN GRAINS</u>. These make the <u>male sex cells</u>.

2) Carpels

1) The <u>female</u> parts of the flower.

2) They contain the <u>stigma</u>, <u>style</u> and <u>ovary</u>.

3) The ovary contains <u>OVULES</u>. These contain the <u>female sex cells</u>.

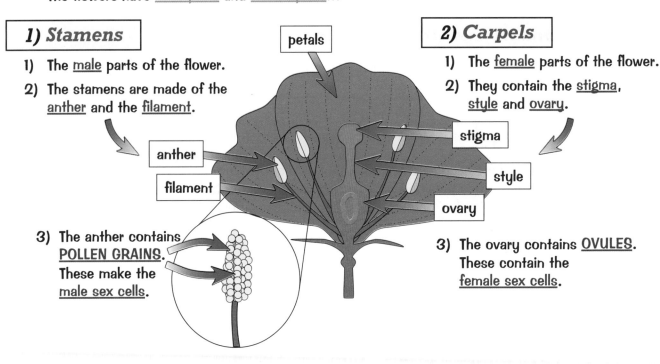

petals
anther
filament
stigma
style
ovary

"Pollination" is Getting Pollen to the Stigma

1) Plants grow from <u>seeds</u>.

2) To make a seed, the <u>male</u> and <u>female sex cells</u> must "<u>meet up</u>".

3) To do this, the <u>pollen grains</u> must get from a <u>stamen</u> to a <u>stigma</u>. This is <u>POLLINATION</u>.

4) Pollen can get from the stamen of <u>one plant</u> to the stigma of a <u>DIFFERENT</u> plant in <u>different ways</u>. For example...

- It can be <u>carried</u> between plants by insects (<u>insect pollination</u>).
- It can be <u>blown</u> between plants by the wind (<u>wind pollination</u>).

Stigma
Stamen

See the next page for more about insect and wind pollination.

Insect Pollination

①
1) Insects <u>visit flowers</u> to get <u>food</u>.
2) They are attracted to a flower by its <u>bright petals</u>.
3) While an insect is at a flower, the <u>pollen</u> <u>sticks to it</u>.

②
When the insect travels to <u>other flowers</u>, it <u>carries the pollen</u> with it.

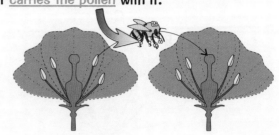

③
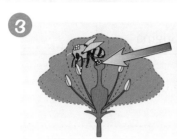

Insect-pollinated flowers have a <u>sticky stigma</u> to pull the pollen off the insect.

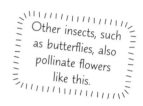
Other insects, such as butterflies, also pollinate flowers like this.

Wind Pollination

<u>Wind-pollinated</u> flowers look quite <u>different</u> from insect-pollinated flowers...

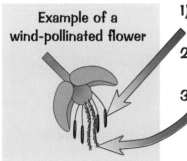
Example of a wind-pollinated flower

1) The <u>anthers</u> of wind-pollinated plants <u>dangle outside</u> the flower.
2) This means <u>pollen</u> gets <u>blown off</u> the anthers when the wind blows.
3) Flowers have a <u>feathery stigma</u> to <u>'catch' the pollen</u> from other flowers as it blows past.

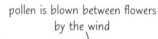
pollen is blown between flowers by the wind

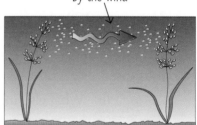

Radical (Plant) Reproduction Questions:

Quick Fire Questions

Q1 Is a stamen a male or a female part of a flower?

Q2 Why do insects visit insect-pollinated flowers?

Practice Questions

Q1 Complete this passage about a plant's sex cells. Use the words below.

male   **female**   **ovary**   **anther**

Ovules contain .... sex cells. The ovules are in the ....

Pollen grains make .... sex cells. Pollen grains are on the ....

Section 3 — Plants and Ecosystems

58

Q2 The diagram below shows the main parts of a flower. The parts of the flower are labelled **A-E**.

(a) The table on the right of the diagram shows information about the parts **A-E**.
Fill in the gaps in the table.

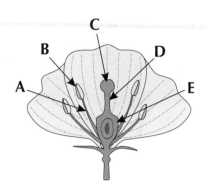

Name of Flower Part	Letter on Diagram	Male or Female?
....	B	Male
Ovary	E	....
Filament	....	Male
....	D	Female
Stigma	....	....

(b) Which **three** letters on the diagram make up the carpel?

....

Q3 Martin picks two flowers in his garden.
The **first** flower has long anthers that hang outside the flower and a feathery stigma.
The **second** flower has bright petals.

(a) Suggest how the **first** flower is likely to be pollinated.

....

(b) (i) Suggest how the bright petals on the **second** flower help it with pollination.

....

(ii) What else might the **second** flower have that could help with pollination?

....

Challenge Yourself

Q4 The picture on the right shows a rose flower.
Describe how rose flowers are pollinated.

Start by thinking about whether the flower is insect-pollinated or wind-pollinated.

....

....

....

....

....

Section 3 — Plants and Ecosystems

Fertilisation and Seed Formation

Once pollen has moved between flowers, the plant can make its seeds. You should know...

- what plant fertilisation is and how it happens
- how seeds and fruit are formed
- what seed dispersal is and some of the ways it can happen.

Fertilisation *is the Joining of Sex Cells*

After pollination, the next step in plant reproduction is fertilisation. Here's how it works...

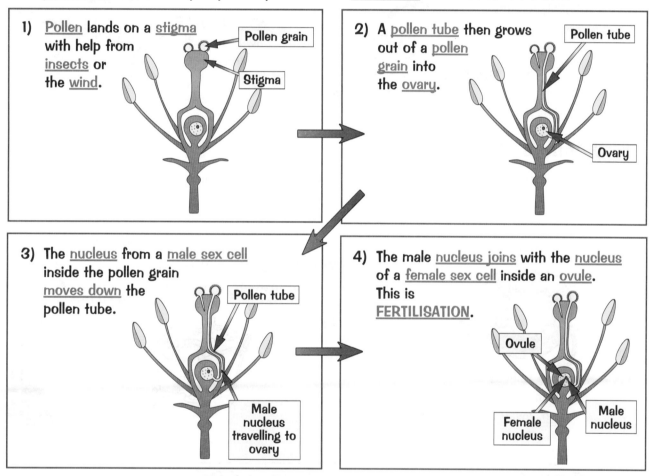

1) Pollen lands on a stigma with help from insects or the wind.

Pollen grain

Stigma

2) A pollen tube then grows out of a pollen grain into the ovary.

Pollen tube

Ovary

3) The nucleus from a male sex cell inside the pollen grain moves down the pollen tube.

Pollen tube

Male nucleus travelling to ovary

4) The male nucleus joins with the nucleus of a female sex cell inside an ovule. This is FERTILISATION.

Ovule

Female nucleus

Male nucleus

Seeds *are Formed From Ovules*

1) After fertilisation, the ovule develops into a seed.

2) The ovary develops into a fruit around the seed, like this:

Fruits aren't just the ones we eat — anything around a seed that grows from the ovary is a fruit.

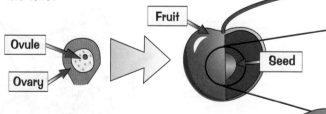

Ovule

Ovary

Fruit

Seed

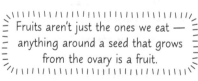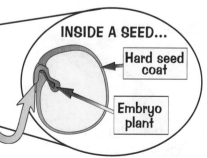

INSIDE A SEED...

Hard seed coat

Embryo plant

3) Each seed contains an embryo plant. This is the part of a seed that grows into a new plant.

Seed Dispersal *is Scattering* Seeds

1) Seeds need to be <u>dispersed</u> (scattered) from the parent plant before they can grow.
2) This is so that they have <u>enough space</u> to grow properly.
3) Here are four <u>different methods</u> of seed dispersal...

The parent plant is the one that made the seeds.

1) Wind dispersal

1) Wind-dispersed seeds are <u>light</u>.
2) Their <u>shape</u> means they <u>catch the wind</u>, so they are carried <u>far away</u> from the parent plant.

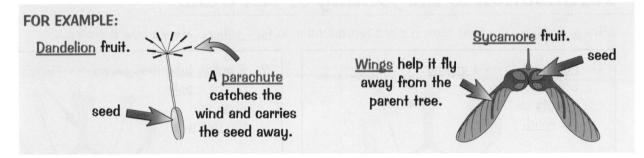

FOR EXAMPLE:

<u>Dandelion</u> fruit.

seed

A <u>parachute</u> catches the wind and carries the seed away.

<u>Sycamore</u> fruit.

<u>Wings</u> help it fly away from the parent tree.

seed

2) Animal dispersal

Fruit is either <u>eaten</u> or <u>carried</u> away from the parent plant by animals.

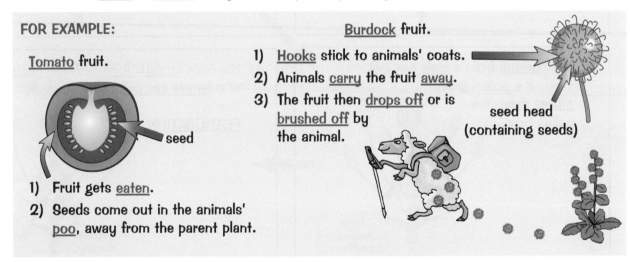

FOR EXAMPLE:

<u>Tomato</u> fruit.

seed

1) Fruit gets <u>eaten</u>.
2) Seeds come out in the animals' <u>poo</u>, away from the parent plant.

<u>Burdock</u> fruit.

1) <u>Hooks</u> stick to animals' coats.
2) Animals <u>carry</u> the fruit <u>away</u>.
3) The fruit then <u>drops off</u> or is <u>brushed off</u> by the animal.

seed head (containing seeds)

3) Explosions

1) These fruits <u>burst</u>.
2) This <u>throws</u> the seeds out, which <u>scatters</u> them.

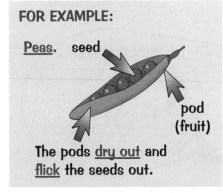

FOR EXAMPLE:

<u>Peas</u>.　seed

pod (fruit)

The pods <u>dry out</u> and <u>flick</u> the seeds out.

4) Drop and Roll

1) The heavy fruit <u>falls</u> down from the tree.
2) It <u>splits</u> when it hits the ground and the seeds <u>roll</u> out.

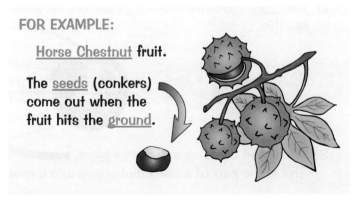

FOR EXAMPLE:

<u>Horse Chestnut</u> fruit.

The <u>seeds</u> (conkers) come out when the fruit hits the <u>ground</u>.

Section 3 — Plants and Ecosystems

Fun Fertilisation and Seed Formation Questions:

Quick Fire Questions

Q1 Which part of a seed grows into a plant?

Q2 Which part of a flower is a fruit made from?

Q3 What method of seed dispersal do pea plants use?

Q4 Name a plant that uses drop and roll to disperse its seeds.

Practice Questions

Q1 The diagram on the right shows a flower just before fertilisation takes place.

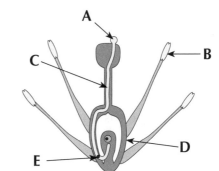

(a) Which letter shows the pollen tube?

....

(b) Draw an X on the diagram to show where **fertilisation** takes place.

(c) What happens at fertilisation? Circle the correct answer.

An embryo plant starts to grow.

The nucleus of a male sex cell and the nucleus of a female sex cell come together.

A pollen grain and an ovule come together.

Q2 Different plants disperse their seeds in different ways.
The sentences below describe four plants.
Draw a line from each sentence to the way the plant is most likely to disperse its seeds.

Description of Plant	Most Likely Way of Dispersing Seeds
A plant that has fruit, which are covered in tiny hooks.	drop and roll
A plant with very light seeds surrounded by feathery strands.	wind
A plant that has seeds in pods, which dry out in the Sun.	animals
A plant that has very heavy fruit.	explosions

Q3 The fruit in the diagram on the right contains a sugary, fleshy layer and has a 'stone' in the middle.

Circle the correct words in bold to make these sentences true.

The stone in the middle of this fruit is actually a **seed / ovary**.

It has developed from one of the plant's **ovules / styles**.

The fruit is sugary to encourage animals to eat it for **seed dispersal / fertilisation**.

Q4 The sentences below describe the stages leading up to a seed being formed.
Put the sentences in the correct order by writing the numbers **1-4** in the boxes beside them.
The first one has been done for you.

☐ A nucleus from a male sex cell travels from the pollen grain to the ovary.

☐ A pollen tube grows down to the ovary.

☐ The nucleus from a male sex cell joins with the nucleus of a female sex cell.

1 A pollen grain lands on a stigma.

Q5 Dandelions grow all over the UK.

(a) How are dandelion seeds dispersed?

....

(b) Describe how the shape of a dandelion fruit helps it to disperse.

....

....

(c) Name another plant that disperses its seeds in a similar way to the dandelion.

....

| Topic Review | How did you get on with the questions? Could you ace a surprise test on this topic? | ☐ ☐ ☐ |

Section 3 — Plants and Ecosystems

Investigating Seed Dispersal Mechanisms

Learning Objective

Ah ha — here comes everyone's favourite bit of science. It's time for an <u>experiment</u>. By the end of these pages, make sure you...
- can <u>investigate</u> how well <u>different seed dispersal methods</u> work.

You Can Investigate Seed Dispersal by Dropping Seeds

You can investigate <u>how well different seeds disperse</u>. It's easiest to investigate <u>wind</u> and <u>drop and roll</u> dispersal.

Here's what you have to do.

1) Get a few different types of <u>fruit</u> (which contain seeds). For example, <u>sycamore fruit</u> and <u>horse chestnut fruit</u>.

2) Decide on a <u>fixed height</u> to drop the fruit from.

3) <u>Drop</u> the fruit <u>one at a time</u> from this height, directly above a <u>set point</u> on the ground.

4) <u>Measure how far</u> along the ground the seeds have travelled from the set point, like this:

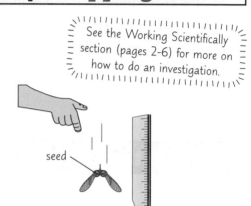

See the Working Scientifically section (pages 2-6) for more on how to do an investigation.

seed

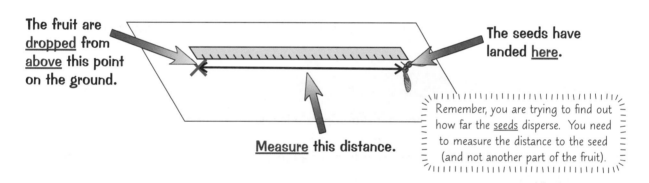

The fruit are <u>dropped</u> from <u>above</u> this point on the ground.

The seeds have landed <u>here</u>.

<u>Measure</u> this distance.

Remember, you are trying to find out how far the <u>seeds</u> disperse. You need to measure the distance to the seed (and not another part of the fruit).

5) <u>Record</u> the distance travelled in a <u>table</u>.

6) Do this experiment <u>three times</u> for each type of seed.

7) Find the <u>mean distance</u> each type disperses. Do this by <u>adding together</u> the three distances for each seed type then <u>dividing</u> each total by three.

Seed Type	Distance Dispersed (cm)			
	1	2	3	mean
Sycamore	20	25	24	(20+25+24) ÷ 3 = 23
Horse Chestnut				

Make Sure it's a Fair Test

You need to keep these things <u>the same</u> each time you do the experiment:

- the <u>person</u> dropping the fruit,
- the <u>height</u> the fruit are dropped from,
- the <u>place</u> you're doing the experiment (<u>stay away</u> from <u>doors</u> and <u>windows</u> that might cause <u>draughts</u>).

This is called "controlling the variables" (see page 3).

Use a *Fan* to Investigate the *"Wind Factor"*

You can investigate <u>how much</u> the <u>wind</u> affects seed dispersal using an <u>electric fan</u>.
Here's how:

1) Set up the fan a <u>fixed distance</u> from the person dropping the fruit.

2) <u>Switch the fan on</u> — it needs to be set to the <u>same speed</u> for every fruit you drop. This makes sure the experiment will be a <u>fair test</u>.

3) <u>Drop</u> the fruit as before and <u>measure</u> how far along the ground the seeds travel (remember to do repeats and calculate an average).

4) If seeds are <u>wind-dispersed</u> they should go <u>much further</u> than other kinds of seed when the <u>fan is on</u>. They should also go further when the fan is <u>on</u> than when it is <u>off</u> (because they do best when it's windy).

Interesting Investigating Seed Dispersal Questions:

Quick Fire Questions

Q1 If you are investigating how well seeds disperse when they fall, how many times should you drop each seed?

Q2 Why is it important to make sure you drop seeds from the same height in an investigation?

Practice Questions

Q1 Amanda is investigating how far different seeds disperse when they are dropped in wind. She has two different fruits — Fruit A and Fruit B. She drops each fruit three times in front of a fan, and records how far each seed travels.

(a) Circle the correct ending to each sentence below.

1. The independent variable in this experiment is

the speed of the fan / the type of fruit Amanda drops.

2. The dependent variable in this experiment is

the distance the seeds travel / the height the fruit is dropped from.

(b) Amanda needs to keep some things the same each time she does this experiment to make sure her results are fair.

Write down **two** things Amanda needs to keep the same during her experiment.

1. ....

2. ....

Section 3 — Plants and Ecosystems

(c) The table below shows Amanda's results. Fill in the missing values.

	Distance Travelled (cm)	
	Seed A	Seed B
Trial 1	11	135
Trial 2	12	122
Trial 3	13	127
Mean	....	....

(d) Amanda notices that all her results from seed A are very close to the mean result.
She notices that her results from seed B are much further away from the mean result.
Do you think Amanda's results are more **precise** for seed A or seed B? Circle your answer.

| Seed A | | Seed B |

(e) Draw a bar chart of the average distances the seeds travelled on the axes below.
Remember to label the axes.

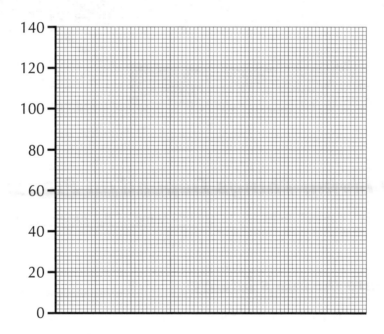

(f) Which type of seed, A or B, is more likely to be dispersed by wind
as it falls from its parent plant? Explain your answer.

....

....

Topic Review How did you find the questions?
Are you happy with the learning objective?

Section 3 — Plants and Ecosystems

66

Dependence on Other Organisms

Learning Objectives Learning Objectives

Plants and animals <u>need each other</u> to <u>survive</u>. Isn't that sweet.
By the end of these pages, you should...

- know that the <u>organisms</u> in an <u>ecosystem</u> are <u>interdependent</u> (and know what that <u>means</u>)
- understand why <u>almost all living things</u> depend on <u>plants</u>
  (for <u>energy</u> and to control <u>gases</u> in the air)
- understand that <u>organisms affect their environment</u> —
  for example, during respiration and photosynthesis
- understand why we need <u>insects</u> to <u>pollinate plants</u>.

Organisms *in an Ecosystem* are *Interdependent*

1) An <u>ecosystem</u> is <u>all</u> the <u>living organisms</u> in <u>one area</u>, plus their <u>environment</u>.

FOR EXAMPLE, A <u>FOREST ECOSYSTEM</u> INCLUDES...

...all of the <u>plants</u>.

...all of the <u>animals</u>.

...the <u>gases</u> in the <u>air</u>.

...the amount of <u>light</u>.

...the <u>temperature</u>.

2) The <u>organisms</u> in an ecosystem are <u>interdependent</u>. This means they <u>need each other</u> to survive.

Almost All Living Things Depend on *Plants*

1) Almost all organisms depend on plants to <u>control some of the gases in the air</u> (see next page).

2) <u>Animals</u> also depend on plants for <u>energy</u> (see below).

Plants Capture the Sun's Energy

1) <u>Almost all energy</u> on <u>Earth</u> comes from the <u>Sun</u>.

2) The Sun gives out <u>light energy</u>. <u>Plants</u> use some of this light energy
   to <u>make food</u> during <u>photosynthesis</u> (see page 53).

3) Plants use the food to build <u>molecules</u> (like <u>proteins</u>) which become part of the plants' cells.

4) These molecules <u>store</u> the Sun's energy.

5) The energy gets <u>passed on from plants</u>
   <u>to animals</u> when animals <u>eat</u> the plants.

6) Animals <u>can't carry out</u> photosynthesis (so they
   <u>can't use light energy</u> straight from the Sun).
   But they do all need <u>energy</u> to stay alive.

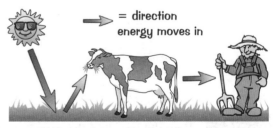

= direction energy moves in

7) So animals <u>need plants</u> to capture the Sun's energy for them.

Section 3 — Plants and EcosystemsSection 3 — Plants and Ecosystems

Plants Give Out Oxygen and Take in Carbon Dioxide

1) When plants and animals <u>respire</u> (see p. 16) they <u>TAKE IN oxygen</u> and <u>GIVE OUT carbon dioxide</u>.

2) During <u>photosynthesis</u>, plants <u>GIVE OUT oxygen</u> and <u>TAKE IN carbon dioxide</u>.

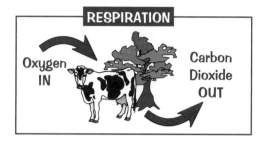 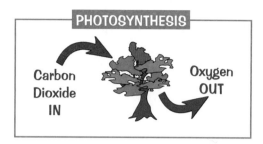

3) Without plants there <u>wouldn't be enough oxygen</u> in the air for <u>respiration</u>.

4) Also, there would be <u>too much carbon dioxide</u> in the air.

Many Plants Depend on Insects to Reproduce

1) We grow <u>crops</u> for food — for example, we grow <u>apple trees</u> to make <u>apples</u>.

2) Many crop plants need insects to <u>pollinate</u> them (see page 57).

3) If plants <u>don't get pollinated</u>, they <u>won't</u> be able to make <u>fruit</u> and <u>seeds</u> for us to <u>eat</u>.

4) So we need insects to pollinate our crops and <u>give us food</u>.

Delightful Dependence Questions:

Quick Fire Questions

Q1 What kind of energy does the Sun give out?

Q2 How do plants store the Sun's energy?

Q3 How do insects help us grow our food?

Practice Questions

Q1 "The organisms in an ecosystem are interdependent." What does this statement mean? Circle the correct answer below.

The organisms in an ecosystem need each other to survive.

The organisms in an ecosystem survive better on their own.

The organisms in an ecosystem get their energy from the Sun.

Q2 What is an ecosystem? Complete the sentence below.

A ecosystem is all the living organisms in one area, plus ....

Section 3 — Plants and Ecosystems

Q3 Complete the following sentences by circling the correct words in bold.

Plants are really important for animals because they control the level of important **gases / light**

in the air. During photosynthesis, plants release **oxygen / carbon dioxide**.

Animals need this for **respiration / nutrition**.

Plants also stop the level of carbon dioxide in the air from getting too **high / low**.

Q4 The picture below shows part of an orchard ecosystem.

plants

animals

(a) Where does the energy in this ecosystem come from?

....

(b) Give **two** parts of this ecosystem that aren't labelled on the picture.

1. ....

2. ....

(c) What process do the apple trees depend on the bees for?

....

(d) (i) The mouse eats seeds from the grass.
Draw **two** arrows on the picture to show how energy gets from the Sun to the mouse.

(ii) Why does the mouse depend on the grass for energy?

....

....

Topic Review How did you find the questions?
Are you happy with all the learning objectives?

Section 3 — Plants and Ecosystems

Food Chains and Food Webs

Food chains and webs are all about <u>what's eating what</u>. It's not very nice but it's very important — most organisms depend on each other for <u>food</u>. Make sure you...

- know what <u>food chains</u> and <u>food webs</u> are
- understand how <u>changes</u> in <u>one part</u> of a food web can <u>affect</u> the <u>rest</u> of the food web
- know that <u>poison</u> can <u>build up</u> along a <u>food chain</u>.

Food Chains Show What *is Eaten by What*

1) This is an example of a <u>food chain</u>:

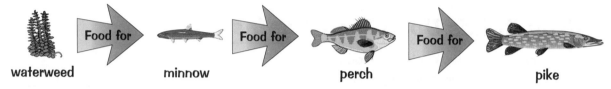

waterweed Food for minnow Food for perch Food for pike

2) The <u>arrows</u> show what is eaten by what. They just mean "<u>food for</u>".
    Here, waterweed is <u>food for</u> minnows. And minnows are <u>food for</u> perch.

3) The arrows also show the direction in which <u>energy</u> gets passed on.
    So, for example, energy in the waterweed gets <u>passed on</u> to the minnows.

Food Webs are *Lots* of *Food Chains* Joined Together

1) There is often <u>more than one</u> food chain in an <u>ecosystem</u>.

2) Look at all these different food chains that you can find in a lake:

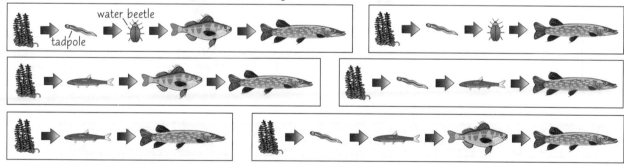

3) You can <u>join</u> these different food chains together to make a <u>food web</u>. Like this...

4) The arrows in a food web still mean "<u>food for</u>". So in this food web,
    <u>tadpoles</u> are food for <u>water beetles</u> AND <u>minnows</u>.

Learn these <u>words</u>:

1. <u>PRODUCER</u> — all <u>plants</u> are <u>producers</u>.
   They 'produce' food energy.
   They always come first in a food chain.

2. <u>CONSUMER</u> — all <u>animals</u> are <u>consumers</u>.
   They eat other living things.

3. <u>PRIMARY CONSUMER</u> —
   an animal that eats <u>producers</u> (plants).

4. <u>SECONDARY CONSUMER</u> — an animal that eats primary consumers.

5. <u>TERTIARY CONSUMER</u> — an animal that eats secondary consumers.

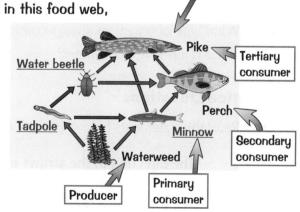

Water beetle Pike Tertiary consumer

Tadpole Perch

Minnow Secondary consumer

Waterweed

Producer Primary consumer

Section 3 — Plants and Ecosystems

A Change *in One Organism* Can Affect *Other Organisms*

1) Food webs make it easier to understand how organisms in an ecosystem are interdependent.

2) The organisms in a food web need each other to survive, so when one organism's numbers fall or rise, it affects other organisms.

Example — What happens if the minnows are removed?

• The number of tadpoles might increase because there are no minnows to eat them.

• The perch might get hungry and start eating more water beetles.
So the number of water beetles might decrease.

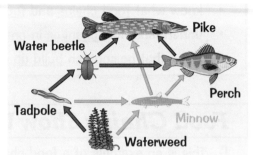

Poison Builds Up in Food Chains

1) Poison can sometimes get into a food chain. For example, a farmer might spray his crops with chemicals to get rid of unwanted insects.

The chemicals that farmers spray their crops with are poisons (substances that can harm or kill an organism).

2) Animals that eat the crop can be affected by the chemical.

3) Animals at the top of the food chain are likely to be the worst affected.

4) This is because the poison builds up as it's passed along the food chain.

= level of poison

Each grain of wheat has a little bit of poison.

Each small bird eats lots of grains of wheat, so they get quite a bit of poison.

Each big bird eats lots of small birds, so they get lots of poison.

Formal Food Chain and Food Web Questions:

Quick Fire Questions

Q1 What is a food web?

Q2 What type of organism always comes first in a food chain?

Q3 What is a primary consumer?

Practice Questions

Q1 Read the statements below and tick the statement that is **true**.

☐ **The direction of the arrows in a food chain doesn't matter.**

☐ **The arrows in a food chain always point from consumer to producer.**

☐ **The arrows in a food chain show the direction of energy flow.**

Q2 The food web below is from a forest ecosystem.

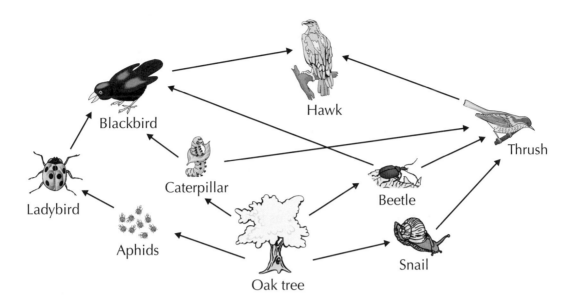

(a) Write down **two** complete food chains from this food web.

1. ....

2. ....

(b) (i) Circle all of the **primary** consumers in this food web.

(ii) Write down the name of **one secondary** consumer in this food web.

....

(c) Draw lines to match each change in the food web to a possible effect.
The first one has been done for you.

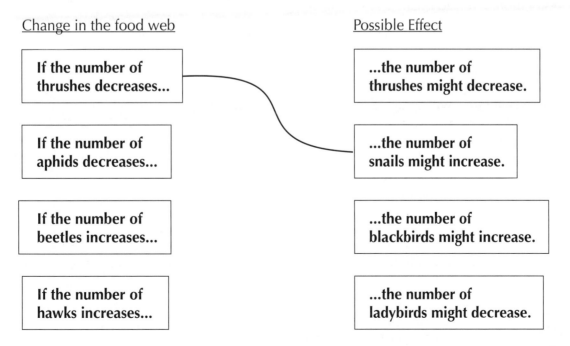

Q3 The diagram below shows part of the food web for a large pond.

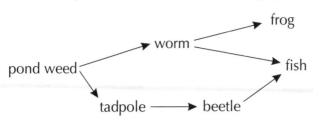

(a) What organism is the producer in this food web?

....

(b) What organisms eat the same food as frogs in this food web?

....

(c) A heron is introduced to the pond. Herons eat frogs.

(i) Write down what effect introducing the heron might have on the number of frogs.

....

(ii) Write down what effect introducing the heron might have on the number of worms.

....

Challenge Yourself

Q4 The food chain on the right is from a wheat field.
The wheat field is sprayed with a poison to kill insects.

High levels of poison in the body of a kestrel mean
that it will lay eggs with thin shells. This makes the
eggs more likely to break and kill the chicks inside.

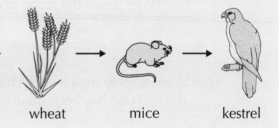

wheat   mice   kestrel

(a) Which organism will have the highest level of poison inside it?

....

(b) What effect will spraying poison have on the number of kestrels in the wheat field?
Explain your answer.

....

....

....

....

Topic Review   How did you get on with the questions?
Are you confident on all the learning objectives?

Section 3 — Plants and Ecosystems

DNA and Inheritance

Learning Objectives

Ever wondered why you have a big nose like your dad? Well, you're in the right place to find out. It's all to do with <u>DNA</u> and <u>inheritance</u>. You need to know...

- what <u>DNA</u>, <u>chromosomes</u>, and <u>genes</u> are
- that you <u>inherit</u> your genes from your <u>parents</u> through <u>heredity</u>
- that <u>Crick</u> and <u>Watson</u> made the first <u>model of DNA</u> using data from <u>Wilkins</u> and <u>Franklin</u>.

DNA, Chromosomes and Genes

1) All living things have <u>DNA</u>.

2) DNA is a long <u>list</u> of <u>chemical instructions</u> on how to build an organism.
   So, for example, a <u>cow's DNA</u> contains all the instructions on how to build a <u>cow</u>.

3) DNA makes up tiny things called <u>chromosomes</u> and <u>genes</u>. Here's how they fit together...

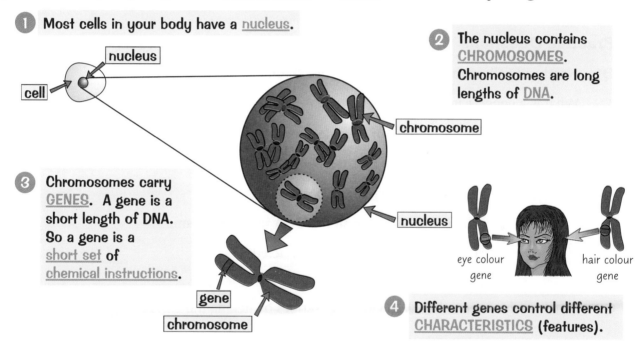

① Most cells in your body have a <u>nucleus</u>.

nucleus

cell

② The nucleus contains CHROMOSOMES.
Chromosomes are long lengths of <u>DNA</u>.

chromosome

nucleus

③ Chromosomes carry GENES. A gene is a short length of DNA. So a gene is a <u>short set</u> of <u>chemical instructions</u>.

gene

chromosome

eye colour gene   hair colour gene

④ Different genes control different CHARACTERISTICS (features).

Genes Are Passed Down From Our Parents

1) During <u>reproduction</u> (see page 43) genes from the mother and father get <u>mixed together</u>, like this:

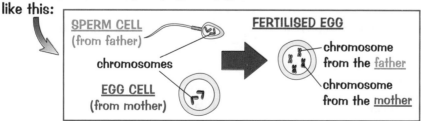

SPERM CELL (from father)

chromosomes

EGG CELL (from mother)

FERTILISED EGG

chromosome from the <u>father</u>

chromosome from the <u>mother</u>

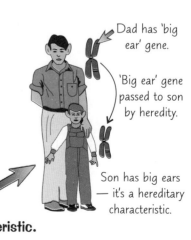

Dad has 'big ear' gene.

'Big ear' gene passed to son by heredity.

Son has big ears — it's a hereditary characteristic.

2) So a baby has an <u>equal mix</u> of its <u>parents' genes</u>.

3) When genes get passed on like this it's called HEREDITY.

4) Remember <u>genes control characteristics</u>.
   So a baby will have a <u>mixture</u> of its <u>parents' characteristics</u>.

5) A characteristic passed on in this way is called a '<u>hereditary</u>' characteristic.

Scientists Worked Out The Structure of DNA

1) <u>Crick</u> and <u>Watson</u> were the <u>first</u> scientists to build a <u>model</u> of DNA.

2) They used <u>data</u> from other scientists called <u>Wilkins</u> and <u>Franklin</u>.

3) This data helped them to <u>understand</u> that a DNA molecule is a <u>spiral</u> made of <u>two chains</u> twisted together.

One chain

Another chain

Dopey DNA Questions:

Quick Fire Questions

Q1 True or false? All living things have DNA.

Q2 Where in a cell is DNA found?

Q3 What are Crick and Watson famous for?

Practice Questions

Q1 Nearly all cells in the human body contain chromosomes and genes.

What is a gene? Circle the correct answer.

A gene is a group of chromosomes.

A gene is a type of cell.

A gene is a short length of DNA.

A gene is the name for all the DNA in an organism.

A gene is another name for the nucleus.

Q2 Match each sentence below to what it describes by ticking the correct box.

(a) Contains all the instructions for building an organism.

☐ **a chromosome**   ☐ **DNA**

(b) A feature passed on from your parents in their genes.

☐ **a hereditary characteristic**   ☐ **a defining characteristic**

(c) A long length of DNA.

☐ **a chromosome**   ☐ **a gene**

(d) The cell structure that contains DNA.

☐ **the nucleus**   ☐ **the cell membrane**

Section 4 — Inheritance, Variation and Survival

Q3 Complete the following sentences. Use words from the box below.

characteristics	chromosomes	cells

Genes and .... are made up of DNA.

Different genes control different ....

Q4 The structure of DNA was discovered in the 1950s.

(a) How did Wilkins and Franklin help this to happen? Circle your answer.

They produced data that was used by Crick and Watson to build a model of DNA.

They used data produced by Crick and Watson to build a model of DNA.

(b) Describe the shape of a DNA molecule.

....

....

Q5 Children have characteristics in common with their mother and their father.

(a) Why do children have characteristics in common with both of their parents?

....

....

(b) What do we call the process by which characteristics are passed on from parents to children?

....

Challenge Yourself

Q6 Emily has a condition that is sometimes called clubbed thumb, which means she has very short thumbs. The condition is controlled by her genes.

Are Emily's short thumbs a **hereditary characteristic**? Explain your answer.

....

....

Topic Review

How did you find the questions?
Are you happy with all the learning objectives?

Section 4 — Inheritance, Variation and Survival

Variation

Different <u>species look different</u> — you wouldn't confuse your pet gerbil with your dog. The <u>members</u> of a <u>species</u> are different too. Make sure you know...

- that <u>different species</u> show variation because of their <u>genes</u>
- that the <u>members of the same species</u> also <u>show variation</u>
- what <u>continuous</u> and <u>discontinuous variation</u> mean, and how these are shown on a <u>graph</u>.

Different Species Have Different Genes

1) <u>VARIATION</u> is the <u>differences</u> between living things.

2) There's variation <u>between different species</u>. This is because they have very <u>different genes</u>, and genes control an organism's <u>characteristics</u>.

3) There's also some variation <u>within a species</u>. There are <u>fewer differences</u> between members of the <u>same species</u> because <u>more</u> of their <u>genes</u> are <u>the same</u>.

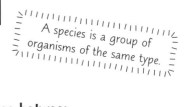

A species is a group of organisms of the same type.

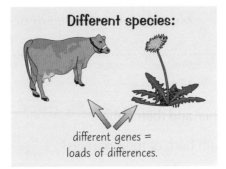

Different species:

different genes = loads of differences.

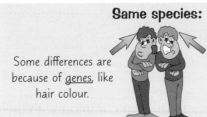

Same species:

Some differences are because of <u>genes</u>, like hair colour.

Some differences are because of our <u>environment</u> (this includes things like the conditions we live in and things that have happened to us in our life). For example, hair style.

Any difference is known as a <u>characteristic feature</u>.

Continuous and Discontinuous Variation

Variation <u>within a species</u> is either <u>continuous</u> or <u>discontinuous</u>.

Continuous Variation — the feature can be any value

1) Examples of this are things like <u>height</u> and <u>weight</u> — these features can be <u>any value</u> within a range.

2) For example, humans can be any <u>height</u> within a range (usually between 150 and 200 cm), not just tall or short.

3) Here is an example of a <u>graph</u> showing <u>continuous variation</u>:

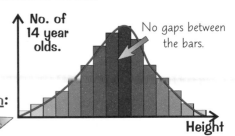

No. of 14 year olds.

No gaps between the bars.

Height

Discontinuous Variation — the feature can only take certain values

1) An example of this is a person's <u>blood group</u>. There are only <u>four separate blood groups</u>. Everyone fits into one of these groups — <u>no one is in between</u>.

2) Another example is the <u>colour of a courgette</u>. A courgette is either yellow, light green or dark green — there's <u>no range</u> of values.

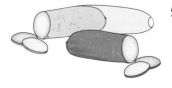

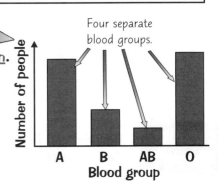

Four separate blood groups.

Number of people

A B AB O
Blood group

Vital Variation Questions:

Quick Fire Questions

Q1 Give **one** example of **continuous variation**.

Q2 Give **one** example of **discontinuous variation**.

Practice Questions

Q1 Which pair of organisms will have the **most differences** between their genes?
Put a tick in the box next to the correct answer.

☐ A mother and her children.   ☐ Two members of different species.

☐ Two members of the same species.   ☐ A father and his children.

Q2 What is a characteristic feature? Circle your answer.

Something all members of the same species have in common.

A special kind of gene.

A difference between members of the same species.

Q3 Farmer Jones records how much milk each of his cows produces in one day.
The graph below shows his results.

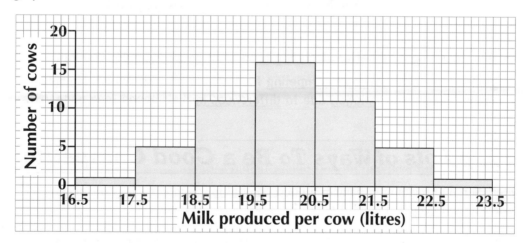

The amount of milk produced varies between cows.
What kind of variation is this? Explain how you know.

....

....

Topic Review Did you feel confident answering the questions?
Have you got all the learning objectives sussed?

 ☐ ☐ ☐

Natural Selection and Survival

The world can be a tough place. Organisms are <u>always competing</u>, and some are better at this than others. By the end of these pages, you should...

- know that organisms <u>compete</u> for resources
- know that some organisms have genes that make them <u>better at competing</u> than others
- understand how this can cause a species to <u>change over time</u> through <u>natural selection</u>.

Organisms Need to Compete

1) Organisms need certain <u>resources</u> so they can <u>survive</u> and <u>reproduce</u>.

2) For example, <u>plants</u> need <u>light</u>, <u>water</u>, and <u>minerals from the soil</u>. <u>Animals</u> need things like <u>food</u>, <u>water</u> and <u>shelter</u>.

3) Often there aren't enough of these resources to go around, so organisms need to <u>compete</u> ('fight') for them.

4) Plants and animals have to <u>compete</u> with: a) other members of <u>their own species</u>, b) organisms from <u>other species</u>.

EXAMPLE

1) <u>Red squirrels</u> have to compete with <u>each other</u> (their own species) for food.

2) They also have to compete with <u>grey squirrels</u> (a different species).

5) Some species are <u>better at competing</u> than others. For example, they might be better at <u>finding food</u> or at <u>hearing danger</u> coming.

6) Some organisms are also <u>better at competing</u> than others from their <u>own species</u>. This is because they show <u>variation</u> due to <u>differences in their genes</u> (see page 76).

There Are Lots of Ways To Be a Good Competitor

The <u>characteristics</u> that make an organism a <u>good competitor</u> depend on lots of things. These include where it <u>lives</u> and what it <u>eats</u>. Here are some examples...

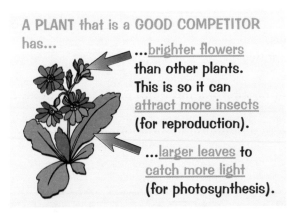

A PLANT that is a GOOD COMPETITOR has...

...<u>brighter flowers</u> than other plants. This is so it can <u>attract more insects</u> (for reproduction).

...<u>larger leaves</u> to <u>catch more light</u> (for photosynthesis).

An OWL that is a GOOD COMPETITOR has...

...<u>better eyesight</u> than other owls to <u>see prey</u>.

"Prey" is an animal eaten by another animal.

...<u>feathers</u> that are a more <u>similar colour</u> to its <u>surroundings</u> than other owls. This means it's <u>less likely</u> to be spotted by other animals that want to <u>eat</u> it.

Variation Leads to Natural Selection

1) Organisms with <u>characteristics</u> that make them <u>better at competing</u> are <u>more likely</u> to <u>survive</u> and <u>reproduce</u>.

2) This means they're more likely to <u>pass on the genes</u> for their useful characteristics to their <u>offspring</u> (children).

3) So, over time, <u>lots of individuals</u> end up with the useful characteristics.

4) When a useful characteristic gradually becomes more common like this, it's called <u>natural selection</u>.

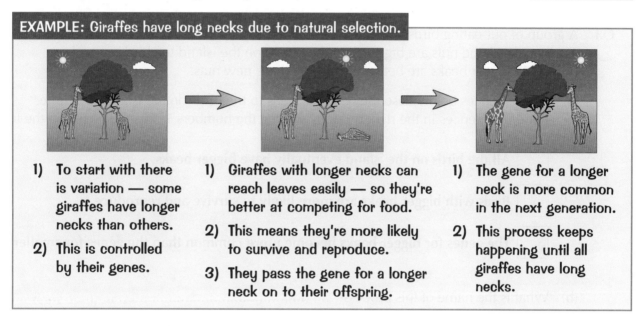

EXAMPLE: Giraffes have long necks due to natural selection.

1) To start with there is variation — some giraffes have longer necks than others.

2) This is controlled by their genes.

1) Giraffes with longer necks can reach leaves easily — so they're better at competing for food.

2) This means they're more likely to survive and reproduce.

3) They pass the gene for a longer neck on to their offspring.

1) The gene for a longer neck is more common in the next generation.

2) This process keeps happening until all giraffes have long necks.

Stunning Natural Selection and Survival Questions:

Quick Fire Questions

Q1 Suggest **two** things a **plant** might compete for.

Q2 Suggest **two** things an **animal** might compete for.

Practice Questions

Q1 Chose the correct words from below to complete the passage that follows.

die	compete	too many	survive
not enough	worse	better	

Plants and animals have to .... for resources because

there are .... to go round. An organism is more likely to

.... and reproduce if it is ....

at competing than other organisms.

Q2   Amanda, Derek and Lisa are watching a robin look for food in their garden.

Amanda says the robin only has to compete with **other robins**.

Derek says the robin has to compete with **other robins and other species of bird**.

Lisa says the robin only has to compete with **other species of bird**.

Who is correct, Amanda, Derek or Lisa?

....

Q3   A group of nut-eating birds move to a new island.
On this island, the nuts are bigger than they were on the island the birds came from.
Birds with bigger beaks are better at cracking these new nuts.

(a)   The sentences below describe what happens to the birds on the island over time.
Put the sentences in the right order by writing the numbers 1-3 in the boxes on the left.

☐   **All the birds on the island eventually have bigger beaks.**

☐   **Birds with bigger beaks are more likely to survive and reproduce.**

☐   **The genes for bigger beaks become more common than the genes for smaller beaks.**

(b)   What is the name of this process?   ....

Challenge Yourself

Q4   Hares are hunted by foxes. Foxes try to creep up on hares.
The foxes then chase the hares if they try to escape.

A scientist studies the hares living in a meadow. The hares show variation.
They can be divided into three groups:

- Group A — these hares have **strong legs** and **big ears**.
- Group B — these hares have **strong legs** and **small ears**.
- Group C — these hares have **small legs** and **small ears**.

In many years time, would you expect most of the hares living in the
meadow to be like those in group A, B or C? Explain your answer.

Start off by thinking about which hares will be the best competitors.

....

....

....

....

....

Topic Review   How did you get on with the questions?
Are you confident on all the learning objectives?   ☹ ☐   😐 ☐   ☺ ☐

Section 4 — Inheritance, Variation and Survival

Extinction and Preserving Species

Learning Objectives

If a species <u>can't compete</u> well enough, it might become <u>endangered</u> or <u>extinct</u> — and that's a shame. You need to...

- understand that <u>species</u> may become <u>extinct</u> if they <u>can't compete successfully</u> when their <u>environment changes</u>
- know what <u>biodiversity</u> is and why we need to <u>protect</u> it
- know what <u>gene banks</u> are and why they are used.

A Species' Environment is Very Important

1) A species' <u>environment</u> is the <u>conditions</u> that it <u>lives in</u>. It includes things like, how <u>hot</u> it is, how often it <u>rains</u> and what other <u>organisms</u> live nearby.

2) If the environment <u>changes</u> in some way, some organisms will be badly affected. They may struggle to <u>compete successfully</u> for the things they need.

3) There are <u>lots of ways</u> that an environment might change. For example:

- <u>Humans</u> could change the environment by clearing trees to make way for <u>farms</u>.
- The environment could get <u>hotter</u> or <u>colder</u>, or <u>wetter</u> or <u>drier</u>.
- A <u>new species</u> could start living in the area. This could mean there is another species to <u>compete with for food</u>.

Many Species Are at Risk of Becoming Extinct

1) If a <u>change in the environment</u> means a <u>whole species</u> can no longer compete successfully, then that species may <u>die out</u>, so there are <u>none of them left at all</u>.

2) This means the species has become <u>extinct</u> (like dinosaurs and the woolly mammoth).

THIS IS WHAT HAPPENED TO THE DINOSAURS...

1) The <u>dinosaurs</u> became <u>extinct</u> about <u>65 million years ago</u>.

2) Some scientists think that this was caused by a <u>huge meteorite</u> (a lump of rock or metal from space) hitting the Earth.

3) They think this caused a <u>massive dust cloud</u>, which <u>blocked</u> out the <u>sun</u>.

4) This would have made the Earth <u>colder</u>. The dinosaurs <u>couldn't survive and reproduce</u> in their new environment, so they died out.

3) Species <u>at risk</u> of becoming extinct are called <u>endangered species</u>. <u>Tigers</u>, <u>pandas</u> and <u>gorillas</u> are all endangered.

Humans *Can* Suffer *When Species Become* Extinct

1) Humans <u>rely</u> on <u>plants</u> and <u>animals</u> for loads of things. For example:

2) We need to <u>protect</u> the organisms we already use.

3) We also need to make sure organisms we <u>haven't discovered yet</u> don't become extinct — they might end up being really important.

4) Organisms <u>rely</u> on other organisms to <u>survive</u> (see page 66). So if one species becomes extinct, this can have a <u>knock-on effect</u> for <u>other species</u> — including <u>humans</u>.

> For example, many of our <u>crops</u> are pollinated by <u>bees</u>. If bees became <u>extinct</u>, it would be harder for us to produce all the <u>food we eat</u> today (see page 67).

5) So it's important that we always have a <u>variety</u> of <u>species</u> on Earth — this is Earth's <u>BIODIVERSITY</u>.

Gene Banks *May Help to* Prevent Extinction

1) Remember, <u>genes</u> are found in <u>cells</u>. They contain the <u>instructions</u> for building an organism.

2) A <u>gene bank</u> is a <u>store</u> of the <u>genes</u> of different species.

3) If a species becomes <u>endangered</u> or <u>extinct</u>, we could use stored genes to <u>create new members</u> of that species.

4) So gene banks could be a way of <u>maintaining biodiversity</u> in the future.

Animal genes can also be stored in gene banks. This is usually done by storing sperm and egg cells.

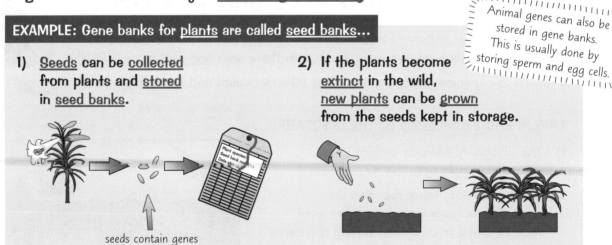

EXAMPLE: Gene banks for <u>plants</u> are called <u>seed banks</u>...

1) <u>Seeds</u> can be <u>collected</u> from plants and <u>stored</u> in <u>seed banks</u>.

2) If the plants become <u>extinct</u> in the wild, <u>new plants</u> can be <u>grown</u> from the seeds kept in storage.

seeds contain genes

Exciting Extinction and Preserving Species Questions:

Quick Fire Questions

Q1 True or False? A species is said to be extinct when there are only two of them left in the wild.

Q2 What is the name for species that are at risk of becoming extinct?

Practice Questions

Q1 What is the Earth's biodiversity? Circle the correct answer.

The number of plants living on the Earth.

The variety of species living on the Earth.

The number of endangered species on the Earth.

Q2 Below are four sentences about biodiversity and protecting species.
Underline **two** sentences that are **false**.

Gene banks might help us to maintain biodiversity in the future.

Changing the environment of all the species on Earth will help to protect them.

We need to protect species because they might be useful in a way we haven't discovered yet.

If a species becomes extinct it will not affect any other species.

Q3 Use words from the box to complete the following passage.

increase	decrease
compete	environment	reproduce

Scientists are worried that climate change may cause a lot of organisms to become extinct.

This is because climate change will cause the .... of many organisms

to change quickly. This will mean lots of them won't be able to ....

successfully for the resources they need. If species do become extinct it will

.... the biodiversity on Earth.

Challenge Yourself

Q4 (a) What is a seed bank?

....

(b) Explain how seed banks could help us to save a species if it becomes extinct.

....

....

....

Topic Review Did you sail through the questions without any trouble?
Do you understand all of the learning objectives?

Section 4 — Inheritance, Variation and Survival

Index

Index

Index